KU-166-638

annabel karmel
Best Ever Cookbook

annabel karmel
Best Ever Cookbook

LONDON, NEW YORK, MUNICH,
MELBOURNE, DELHI

Senior editor Ros Walford
DTP Designer Kavita Varma
Senior production controller Kate Klahn
Associate publisher Nigel Duffield
Recipe testing Caroline Stearns
Editorial consultant Karen Sullivan
Allergy consultant Dr Adam Fox
Breastfeeding consultant Joanna
Moorhead
Nutritional consultant Dr Rosan Meyer
Paediatric consultant Dr Su Laurent
Food styling Valerie Berry, Katie Giovanni,
Seiko Hatfield
Home economists Jayne Cross,
Carolyn Humphries
Photographers Dave King, Michael Birt
Photography art direction Carole Ash,
Luis Peral

Every effort has been made to ensure that the
information contained in this book is complete and
accurate. However, neither the publisher nor the author
are engaged in rendering professional advice or services
to the individual reader. The ideas, procedures, and
suggestions contained in this book are not intended as a
substitute for consultation with your healthcare provider.
All matters regarding the health of you and your child
require medical supervision. Neither the publisher
nor the author accept any legal responsibility for any
personal injury or other damage or loss arising from the
use or misuse of the information and advice in this book.

First published in Great Britain in 2010 by Dorling Kindersley,
80 Strand, London WC2R 0RL. A Penguin Company.

Contains content from *Your Feeding Questions Answered*
(© 2009; Text © 2009 Annabel Karmel), *Baby and Toddler
Diary* (© 2008; Text © 2008 Annabel Karmel).

Copyright © 2010 Dorling Kindersley Limited.
Text copyright © 2010 Annabel Karmel.

All rights reserved. No part of this publication may be
reproduced, stored in a retrieval system, or transmitted
in any form, electronic, mechanical, photocopying,
recording or otherwise, without the prior written
permission of the copyright owners.

A CIP catalogue record is available from the British Library.

ISBN: 978-1-4053-6230-6

Printed and bound by LEO Paper Group in China

Discover more at
www.dk.com

contents

foreword

As parents, we all worry about whether we're bringing up our children the right way. It's really hard to know what is best: Is it OK to give an occasional bottle if you're breastfeeding your baby? At what age should you introduce solid food? When is the right time to give your baby a cup? How do you know when your little one is ready for finger foods?

I have written this book to guide you through each stage of feeding your baby and toddler, up to three years of age, by answering all the common questions that concern mums. Whatever the problems you may encounter along the way, they are sure to be shared with other mums. Reading this book will give you an insight into what to expect, as well as lots of tips and advice on how to cope with all manner of feeding issues.

Right from the start breastfeeding can be a challenge and it can be easy to give up – especially in those often difficult first few days. However, with the right advice, you will soon find that breastfeeding is much easier and more enjoyable than you ever imagined, so persevere!

Introducing a baby to solid food is a confusing time, as there is so much conflicting advice. I find that parents are often so worried about food allergies that they keep their babies on very restricted diets of fruit and vegetables, because they're concerned about introducing foods such as eggs, fish, and meat. However, babies will not thrive on low-calorie, restricted diets – they need iron from red meat, essential fatty acids from oily fish and, unlike adults, they need more fat and less fibre in their diets. The advice I give in this book is based on the latest medical research from the UK's top experts. I want to give mums and dads the confidence to know that they are giving their babies the food they need to grow and develop.

Since I lost my first child Natasha twenty years ago, I have devoted my life to researching child nutrition. I have written 17 books and I work with the top experts in the field of child nutrition. With the knowledge I have gained over the years, I find ways to encourage children to eat the foods that are good for them by including them in tasty recipes, which are easy to prepare. Combining my own experiences as a mum of three with the latest scientific research, I hope that this book will help to guide you through your baby's first few years, and give you the peace of mind to know that you are giving your child the very best start in life.

Annabel Karmel

early nutrition

Babies and toddlers have little tummies, so everything you serve them should be packed with **the nutrients they need** to become **strong and healthy**. What they eat forms the foundation of their health for years to come.

From birth until about six months, babies get everything they need from breast or formula milk. Babies grow and develop rapidly in the first years, so it's important for the mother to ensure they get a variety of nutrients in the form of carbohydrates, fat, protein, and vitamins and minerals (see chart, pages 12–13). Food must also meet their energy (calorie) needs for healthy development.

• carbohydrates

Carbohydrates are "energy" foods, and they provide your baby with his main source of fuel. Initially babies are weaned onto easy-to-digest refined carbohydrates like fortified cereals. When they are older they can be introduced to more complex carbohydrates, such as wholegrain breads, breakfast cereals and pastas, brown or wild rice, and other wholegrain products. These foods provide a range of nutrients (such as the B vitamins) as well as fibre, and have the advantage of breaking down

★ How much should you give every day?

✳ 3–5 servings of protein
2–3 of which should be from meat, poultry, fish, or pulses, and 2 servings should be from dairy products.

✳ 4–5 servings of healthy carbohydrates
Young babies need to have refined carbohydrates; from about 1 year you can introduce complex carbohydrates.

✳ 5 servings of fruit and vegetables Fruit and vegetables should form part of every meal and should also be provided as snacks between meals.

✳ What is a serving? There are no precise guidelines on portion sizes for children. You can estimate protein portions by looking at your child's hand: a portion of red meat, poultry, or pulses is the size of his palm; a fish portion is the size of his whole hand. Add carbohydrates and vegetables/fruit at least in equal amounts. If your child wants to eat more, increase carbohydrates and vegetables/fruit before increasing protein.

slowly in your child's body and therefore keeping him satisfied for a longer period. Refined carbohydrates like cakes, sweet biscuits, and other sugary foods should be avoided as they supply few nutrients, but lots of "empty calories".

• protein

Protein is found in fish, lean meats, poultry, pulses (such as chickpeas, beans, and lentils), soya, dairy produce, eggs, and some wholegrains. It supplies your baby with the building blocks for growth and healthy development. It is also essential for maintaining body functions.

• fat

Fat is the most calorie-dense component of food and is necessary for growth and essential nutrients required for brain function. Fats also contain the vitamins A, D, and E, which are necessary for many body processes. When babies are breastfed, over 50 per cent of calories come from fat. Once babies are weaned, they still need more fats than adults to ensure that they grow and develop properly. Most important are the essential fatty acids, known as EFAs or "omega" oils, which are found in oily fish, nuts, seeds, olive and some vegetable oils, and avocados. These are important for brain and visual development and immune function. Research has shown that one of the EFAs from oily fish can improve children's behaviour and their ability to learn. Not all fats are the same, however, and some should be eaten in smaller quantities than others (see pages 10–11).

• water

Water is essential to the digestive process – both ensuring that there is adequate saliva for digestion and that waste products are eliminated properly. Without water, your baby's cells cannot build new tissue efficiently, toxic products build up in his bloodstream, and less oxygen and nutrients will be transported to his cells, all of which can leave him weak, tired, and at risk of illness.

• fibre

Fibre has a host of roles in your baby's body, which encourage it to function properly. Fibre literally acts as a broom, clearing away debris from the digestive tract and keeping it healthy. It also adds bulk to your baby's diet, which contributes to healthy bowel function. In addition, fibre stimulates the flow of saliva, which protects teeth and encourages healthy digestion. Fibre is found in almost all fruits, vegetables, and grains – one reason these foods are so important to health.

• prebiotics

Prebiotics are non-digestible food ingredients that aid absorption of nutrients, reduce intestinal infections, and improve immunity. Good sources are wheatgerm, oats, onions, garlic, and leeks.

healthy eating

Creating **a healthy diet for your child** is easier than you may think. Giving your child balanced, healthy meals will set a good example for him later on in life. **Here are a few key tips** to remember.

• go for five a day

Fruit and vegetables are essential for healthy babies and children. They offer a range of vitamins, minerals, fibre, some proteins and complex carbohydrates, and are naturally low in or free from unhealthy fat. It's easy to purée a few different fruits and vegetables together for your baby, and make sure you offer your child fruit as snacks and alongside every meal to ensure that he's getting enough.

• offer variety

If your child eats the same things day after day, chances are he'll be missing out on a few key nutrients. Brightly coloured fruits and vegetables have different nutrients to leafy greens, for example. Aim to give your child a little of everything. Try different grains: offer sweet potato or butternut squash in place of white potatoes, and offer berries or mango instead of apples and bananas from time to time.

• keep sugar to a minimum

Sugar not only damages your baby's teeth (which can also affect his adult teeth), but also impacts on mood, immunity, sleep patterns, and weight. You don't want your child to become used to high levels of sugar and develop a "sweet tooth". If your child is over 12 months, honey can be added to foods in moderation. Children can very easily grow to love the natural sweetness of fruits and vegetables when they become used to them.

• watch out for salt

Don't add salt to your child's food. Little ones become accustomed to salty food and find healthy, unrefined foods bland without it. Children need no more than 1750mg of salt every day, and chances are they are getting more than that in their diets at present. You'll find hidden salt in foods such as bread, breakfast cereals, and even cheese. Too much salt affects children's body-water balance and can also influence the absorption of nutrients. Don't let salt creep into your child's diet.

• "good" fat versus "bad" fat

Fats, particularly EFAs (see page 9), are essential for little ones, but you want to aim for unsaturated fats, such as olive and vegetable oils, nuts, seeds, avocado, and oily fish, which are known to be beneficial to health. When eaten in excess, saturated fats, such as those found in butter, hard cheese, lard, and meat, have been linked to obesity, asthma, some cancers, and heart disease in later life, and should be offered in much smaller quantities than the unsaturated varieties. Babies and toddlers need fat in their diet, including saturated fat, but it's important to get the balance right. Avoid transfats, which are oils that have been "hydrogenated" to make them spreadable. These fats may contribute to obesity and heart disease and are used in all kinds of processed and baked food, including biscuits, crisps, and cakes.

• reducing obesity

Obesity is a concern for a growing number of parents. About 27 per cent of children above two years of age in the UK are now classified as being too heavy for their age and height, and the childhood obesity rate in the United States has almost doubled for preschool children aged 2–5 years. Learn to listen to your child. If he isn't hungry, don't push it.

daily nutritional requirements

This chart sets out the amounts of vitamins and minerals recommended for children. A balanced diet, with plenty of good-quality protein, healthy fat, complex carbohydrates, and fresh vegetables and fruit will give all the vitamins and minerals your child needs.

nutrient	source	benefit	amount
vitamin A	wholegrains, nuts, seeds, meat (especially pork), corn, pulses, certain vegetables	needed for good immunity, good vision, and healthy skin	0–12 months 350mcg; 1–3 years 400mcg 30g (1oz) carrots = 380mcg
vitamin B$_1$ (thiamin)	milk and milk products, eggs, liver, green vegetables, pulses	helps with carbohydrate metabolism and normal functioning of nervous system	0–6 months 0.2mg; 7–12 months 0.3mg; 1–3 years 0.5mg 30g (1oz) lentils = 0.5mg
vitamin B$_2$ (riboflavin)	liver, lean red meat, fortified breakfast cereals, eggs	helps with energy release from food and iron transport in the body; keeps skin healthy	0–6 months 0.2mg; 7–12 months 0.4mg; 1–3 years 0.6mg 1 egg = 0.16mg
vitamin B$_3$ (niacin)	apricots, leafy green vegetables, carrots, liver, oily fish, eggs, butter, cheese, cereal, oat porridge	helps with normal functioning of nervous system, keeps body's cells healthy	0–6 months 2mg; 7–12 months 4mg; 1–3 years 6mg 30g (1oz) cereal = 5.5mg
vitamin B$_{12}$	fish, milk and milk products, meats, eggs	forms red blood cells, increases energy, improves concentration, maintains nervous system	0–6 months 0.3mcg; 7–12 months 0.4mcg; 1–3 years 0.5mcg 30g (1oz) beef = 2.1mcg
vitamin C	fresh fruit, especially berries, and vegetables, potatoes, leafy herbs	vital for healthy skin, bones, muscles, healing, and protection from viruses, allergies, and toxins; helps the body absorb iron	0–12 months 25mg; 1–3 years 30mg 30g (1oz) potatoes = 10mg
vitamin D	milk and milk products, eggs, oily fish	increases absorption of calcium from diet; essential for growth and health of bones and teeth	0–6 months 8.5mcg; 7 months to 3 years 7mcg 30g (1oz) sardines = 5.8mcg
vitamin E	nuts, seeds, eggs, milk, wholegrains, unrefined oils, leafy vegetables, avocados	needed for metabolism of essential fatty acids; protects cells of the body	0–3 years 6mg 30g (1oz) avocado = 0.6mg

a healthy diet

Vegetables and fruit are rich in vitamins and minerals. Encourage your toddler to eat plenty by giving him manageable pieces that he can pick up with his fingers.

nutrient	source	benefit	amount
folate	leafy green vegetables, wheatgerm, pulses, liver, milk	needed for cell maintenance and repair; forms blood cells; crucial to the functioning of the nervous system	0–12 months 525mcg; 1–3 years 350mcg 30g (1oz) broccoli = 9mcg
calcium	milk and milk products, leafy green vegetables, sardines, sesame seeds, root vegetables	required for healthy bones, teeth, and muscles	0–12 months 525mg; 1–3 years 350mg 30g (1oz) hard cheese = 75mg
iron	liver, meat, poultry, dark chocolate, sardines and other fish, pulses, dark green leafy vegetables, raisins, dried apricots, fortified cereals	needed for production of haemoglobin (the oxygen-carrying part of blood) and certain enzymes; necessary for immune activity	0–3 months 1.7mg; 4–6 months 4.3mg; 7–12 months 7.8mg; 1–3 years 6.1–8.7mg 30g (1oz) poultry = 0.5mg
magnesium	brown rice, soya beans, nuts, brewer's yeast, wholegrains, milk, pulses	repairs body cells; needed for energy metabolism; maintains nerve and muscle function; keeps bones strong; promotes normal blood pressure	0–3 months 55mg; 4–6 months 60mg; 7–9 months 75mg; 10–12 months 80mg; 1–3 years 85mg 30g (1oz) brown rice = 13.2mg
potassium	bananas, potatoes, citrus fruit, dried fruit, milk and milk products	essential for muscle and heart function; helps with maintaining the baby's fluid balance	0–6 months 78–85mg; 7–12 months 70mg; 1–3 years 78mg 1 banana = 358mg
selenium	seafood and fish, poultry, meat, wholegrains, nuts, brown rice, pulses, eggs	required by the immune system; improves liver function; needed for healthy eyes, skin, and hair; protects against heart and circulatory diseases	0–6 months 6mcg; 7–12 months 10mcg; 1–3 years 15mcg 30g (1oz) white fish= 1.28mcg
zinc	seafood, poultry, lean red meats, sunflower seeds, peanuts, wholegrains, pulse	required for healthy body cells, immunity, growth, and energy metabolism	0–6 months 4mg; 7–36 months 5mg 30g (1oz) pulses = 0.39mg

food allergies

There's a lot of confusion about which foods can be given to babies. It seems that every day we hear a new story about the dangers that some foods pose to children. But **what are food allergies** and how common are they?

Introducing first foods to your baby should be a fun stage in your baby's development. Yet many parents regard this stage as a potential minefield, so anxious are they about allergic reaction to different foods.

The reality is that only a small proportion of people are affected by allergies. Approximately 6–8 per cent of young children and 3.7 per cent of adults in the UK and US have a food allergy. The difference between these figures is due to the fact that many children grow out of their allergies by school age.

The most common food allergies in children are to milk and eggs (the world over); peanuts (in the UK, North America, and Australia); and shellfish and fish (in South East Asia and Japan).

• when to worry

There is no need to worry unduly about food allergies unless there is a history of allergy in your family or your baby suffers from eczema. If this is not the case, it is fine to start introducing foods like meat, chicken, fish, and eggs to your baby from around six months, once you have given a variety of fruits and vegetables. I find that a lot of parents restrict their baby's diet, when in fact it's really important to give them these nutrient-rich foods, as they need iron and essential fatty acids from six months.

However, if your family has a history of allergy (such as hayfever, asthma, eczema, or a food allergy), and particularly if your baby suffers from eczema, your baby has an increased risk of developing a food allergy. The more severe the eczema, the greater the chance. You should try to breastfeed exclusively for the first six months and then introduce low-allergen foods (for example root vegetables, apple, pear, or baby rice) for the first few weeks. New foods should be introduced one at a time and given for two or three consecutive days so that if there is a reaction, you will know what has caused it. If your child is found to be allergic to a basic food, like cow's milk or egg, seek advice from a doctor or registered dietician on how to keep meals balanced.

• what are food allergies?

A food allergy occurs when the immune system produces allergy antibodies (known as IgE) to certain foods. These antibodies detect when the particular food has been eaten and instead of letting the body ignore it, they cause an overreaction involving the release of a chemical called histamine. Histamine causes an itchy rash, swelling and, in severe cases, difficulty in breathing. Reactions tend to occur immediately or very soon after touching or eating the food. This type of

tips

* **If there is no history** of allergy in your family, your child is unlikely to be affected.

* **If your child has eczema** in the early stages of her life, she is at increased risk of food allergy.

* **Berry fruits** can cause redness around the mouth in kids with eczema. This is rarely due to allergy.

allergy is relatively well understood by doctors. Some foods, such as cow's milk, soya, wheat, and eggs, can cause delayed allergic reactions. These also tend to affect babies and young children and can cause symptoms such as eczema and diarrhoea, although relatively little is known about them at present.

• immediate food allergies

Immediate reactions to food occur straight after it is eaten or up to two hours later. They are often fairly mild and can include hives and facial swelling. A severe reaction can include coughing, wheezing, shortness of breath, noisy breathing, collapse, and loss of consciousness (caused by a drop in blood pressure, known as shock). This is an anaphylactic reaction and requires urgent medical attention. Other immediate symptoms can include cramping tummy pains and vomiting.

Most immediate food allergies are due to milk egg, peanuts, tree nuts, fish, shellfish, wheat, soya, and sesame. Allergies to milk, egg, wheat, and soya are usually outgrown, but those to peanuts, tree nuts, fish, and shellfish tend to remain for life.

• nut allergy

Recent reports suggest that almost 1 in 50 UK children suffers from a nut allergy, including to peanuts. Peanut allergy is the commonest nut allergy (it seems to have doubled in a decade), and is the main cause

of anaphylaxis due to food in the UK and US. The advice for parents trying to avoid nut allergies developing in their children has been the cause of some controversy. Pregnant women with a history of allergy (or with an allergic child or partner) are advised that they may wish to avoid peanuts during pregnancy and breastfeeding, as well as excluding them from their child's diet for the first three

If your child reacts ...

* **Any immediate severe reaction** that includes wheezing, breathing difficulties, throat swelling, collapse, or loss of consciousness is referred to as an anaphylactic reaction. This is rare, but life-threatening. Call an ambulance immediately.

* **If you think your child shows signs** of a mild or delayed allergic reaction, see your GP, who can discuss this with you and can refer you to a specialist if necessary.

years of their life. However, recent research suggests that this may not be helpful in stemming the rise in peanut allergies. Some studies suggest that peanut allergies might be prevented if babies were exposed to peanuts in their diet during weaning. The jury is still out and more research is required, but it's safe to say that if there is a family history of allergy or if your baby has severe eczema, seek medical advice before introducing nuts and nut products to your baby. However, if there is no history of allergy then it is fine to introduce peanut butter and finely ground nuts into your baby's diet from six months.

• egg allergy

Egg allergies are less common than people think and children who do develop them tend to grow out of them by age six. Opinions vary, but experience has taught me that a whole egg is a perfectly healthy food for your baby from six months, provided it is fresh and cooked until solid. Children with a family history of allergy and those who suffer from eczema are more likely to have an egg allergy.

• delayed food allergies

Some children have persistent, less-obvious reactions to certain foods. These delayed allergies involve a different part of the immune system that responds more slowly.

The foods most commonly involved in delayed food allergies are cow's milk and, less often, soya, wheat, and egg. The reaction to the food may take up to 48 hours to appear. Symptoms can include worsening of eczema, diarrhoea (possibly with blood and mucus), and poor weight gain. These allergies can be difficult to diagnose, as sufferers may continue to eat and drink the problem food.

Delayed food allergies are sometimes mistakenly called food intolerances. Food intolerances, however, are reactions to food, such as tummy upsets and diarrhoea, that, unlike allergies, don't involve the immune system. They tend to be more of an issue for adults than children.

★ diagnosing allergies

✳ **If you suspect an allergy**, you must see a doctor with experience in allergy. Do not attempt to diagnose it yourself.

✳ **The best way to diagnose an** immediate food allergy is with a skin prick test and/or a blood test. Both are used to detect the presence of antibodies called IgE, which helps to identify the problem foods. Results of these tests need to be carefully interpreted by an experienced doctor to avoid unnecessary food exclusions.

✳ **The most accurate way to** diagnose a delayed food allergy is to eliminate the suspected food(s) for a minimum of two weeks and see if symptoms cease. Reintroduce the foods one at a time, under the supervision of a doctor or a registered dietician, and see if the symptoms reappear. Keeping a food and symptom diary can help pinpoint which foods are the cause.

✳ **There are many private tests available,** such as hair analysis and kinesiology. None of these are accurate – they are costly, and can put your child's health at risk.

kitchen essentials

Weaning can be daunting, but there are **plenty of tools** and shortcuts to **make life easier.** Learn how to freeze baby food safely to avoid cooking every day, and a little about **food hygiene** to help **keep your baby healthy.**

• equipment

You will probably find that you already have most of the equipment you need to make home-cooked meals, but below are a few items that will make preparing food for your child a little easier.

✳ **A mouli** or baby food grinder is good for foods that have a tough skin, like peas or dried apricots, as it produces a smooth purée, while holding back the indigestible bits.

✳ **Steamers** are great for cooking vegetables as steaming is the best way to preserve nutrients.

✳ **Electric hand blenders** are ideal for making baby purées and can handle small quantities of food.

✳ **Food processors** are good for puréeing larger quantities when making batches of purées for freezing. Many also have mini bowl attachments, which work better with smaller quantities.

✳ **A masher and bowl** is quick and easy when your baby moves on to lumpier foods.

✳ **A microwave steamer** with a valve in the lid that allows steam to be released is ideal for cooking fish or vegetables.

✳ **Freezer pots** with snap-on lids are handy and can be used as extra feeding bowls.

✳ **Ice cube trays** are great for freezing meal-sized portions of purées.

✳ **A feeding kit for babies** should include small heat-proof plastic weaning bowls, shallow soft-tipped weaning spoons, a feeding cup with a spout and two handles, and washable or wipe-clean plastic bibs.

• kitchen hygiene

Food hygiene is important for everyone, but babies and young children are especially vulnerable to the effects of food poisoning, so it is essential that you take care in storing and preparing food.

Raw meat, poultry, fish, and other raw foods can easily cross-contaminate other foods. After handling these, wash your hands, utensils, and surfaces thoroughly. Use three chopping boards in different colours: one for raw, one for cooked, and one for smelly foods, such as garlic. Keep raw and cooked foods apart in your fridge, with raw placed on the bottom shelf.

Using a dishwasher is generally far more hygienic than washing up by hand as it operates at a higher temperature and dries by steam rather than a tea towel, which can harbour bacteria. Only your baby's bottle and teat need to be sterilized. Wipe your child's highchair with an anti-bacterial surface cleaner.

If using jars of baby food, decant the amount of food you need into a bowl and save the rest. Once a spoon with saliva has mixed with the food, you will need to use up or throw away the contents.

Don't leave perishable food out of the fridge for more than two hours and use up baby food that is stored in the fridge within 24 hours.

• freezing and reheating

As your baby eats only very small quantities, especially in the early stages, it saves time to make larger batches of your baby's purée and freeze extra portions in ice cube trays or plastic freezer pots for future meals. In a couple of hours you can prepare enough food for your baby for a month. Once food has cooled down, freeze it as soon as possible and label it with the contents and expiry date. Purées will keep for eight weeks in the freezer.

Thaw foods by defrosting them in the fridge overnight or by taking them out of the freezer several hours before a meal.

Always reheat foods until piping hot. Allow to cool and test the temperature before giving it to your baby. If reheating in a microwave, make sure that you stir the food to get rid of any uneven "hot spots". Do not reheat food more than once and never refreeze meals that have already been frozen.

★ helpful hints

✱ Keep a kitchen notepad so that you can jot down foods that you're running low on.

✱ Keep spares of basic ingredients, such as flour, tinned tomatoes, and vegetable oil, and when you run out of the first tin or bottle, put it on the list. Keep basics such as bread and chicken breasts in the freezer.

✱ To extend their shelf life, store foods such as flour, nuts, and dried fruit in sealed containers. This helps to isolate bugs too.

✱ Save yourself time and shop for basic ingredients online.

✱ The temperature of your freezer should be -18°C (0°F) and your fridge 4°C (40°F).

✱ Make your own combinations of purées by mixing two single ingredients together, such as a cube each of carrot and apple purée to make an apple and carrot purée.

feeding your baby

Feeding your baby isn't just about **satisfying her hunger.**
Whether breast- or bottlefeeding, you will be spending many
hours with your baby – **it's a time for cuddles** and for enjoying
a real feeling of closeness.

Breast milk is the most natural food for your baby, so it's worth breastfeeding even for a week, as your breasts produce colostrum for the first three or four days. This thick yellow fluid is high in antibodies, which help protect your baby against infection before her immune system can start functioning properly. After two to four days, milk production is established and colostrum gradually changes into mature milk (see box, below).

Formula milk is made of modified cow's milk and, however hard manufacturers try, they can never mimic human breast milk – it doesn't contain the antibodies that breast milk has. However, if you are unable to breastfeed or are uncomfortable with it, you can still give your baby a good start with formula milk.

• beginning breastfeeding

Feeds can last from 10 to 40 minutes, so sit in a comfortable chair that supports your back. Keep a glass of water nearby, as breastfeeding can make you feel thirsty. It is important that your baby takes the nipple and a good proportion of the areola surrounding it into her mouth in order to stimulate your breast to produce milk. If it feels uncomfortable, insert your little finger in your baby's mouth and start again. Make sure your baby has completely emptied the first breast before putting her on the second. Some babies need about 30 minutes to empty the breast.

★ Why is it so important to breastfeed my baby?

Breast milk is packed with antibodies and strengthens babies' immune systems, which is particularly important for premature babies. It is rich in omega-3 essential fatty acids, which are important for brain development, and contains prebiotics that help with the development of gut immunity. It is believed that breastfeeding for just one month has health benefits for the first 14 years of your child's life. Research has shown it protects babies from ear, chest, and gastrointestinal infections, asthma, childhood diabetes, eczema, and even obesity. The composition of breast milk changes to meet all your baby's needs; firstly quenching her thirst and then providing her with calories and nutrients.

chapter 1

0–6 months:
your new baby and you

0–6 months:
what you can expect

Your new baby will gradually settle into a routine of feeding and sleeping, growing more alert and **investigating her world** as she stays awake for longer periods. Your baby will grow more in this period than **at any other time in her life.** Settle in and enjoy the process of bonding.

Q Why is it so important to breastfeed for the first few days?

A While the longer you breastfeed your baby, the greater the benefits, you'll be giving your baby a better start even if you can manage it just for a few days. Breast milk is designed to provide complete nourishment for a baby for at least six months after birth. Before milk is produced a mother's breasts produces colostrum, a deep-yellow liquid containing high levels of protein, nutrients, and antibodies. A newborn baby who feeds on colostrum in the first few days of life is better able to resist the bacteria and viruses that cause illness. Your milk, which begins to flow a few days after childbirth when your hormones change, is a blue-white colour with a thin consistency and provides the perfect balance of nutrients for your baby. Some mums are alarmed that it looks "weak" or even "skimmed" next to the rich, yellowy colour of formula milk, but it is important to remember that it's been designed this way for a reason, and provides easily digestible nutrients that are just right for a baby.

Q How often do babies need to be fed?

A Your baby's appetite and needs will change constantly as she grows and develops, and it is important that she is fed when she is hungry. At the outset, you may be feeding your newborn every two hours or so, but it is almost impossible to overfeed a breastfed baby. For the first month of life, your baby needs between 8 and 12 feeds every day. As she grows and begins to take more at feeding time, she will go a little longer – sometimes up to three or four hours – between feeds. As you get to know your new baby, you'll recognize her signs of hunger, and know when she needs to be fed.

Q Is milk all my baby needs for the first six months?

A Breast milk and/or formula milk are perfectly designed to be a complete food for babies, providing them with nutrients, such as protein, fat, carbohydrates, vitamins and minerals, calories, as well as liquid to keep them hydrated. In the case of breast milk, your baby will get some additional benefits, such as antibodies against infections, as well as hormones, EFAs (essential fatty acids), enzymes, and living cells which fight infection. If you are bottle-feeding, EFAs and other elements, such as probiotics, may also be added to your baby's formula to ensure your baby's health. At present, the UK government and the WHO (World Health Organization) recommend exclusive breastfeeding for six months, but you may feel that your baby is ready for solids a little earlier than this (see pages 52–53). If this is the case, speak to your health visitor or GP.

★ your baby's tummy

Your baby's tummy is smaller than you may think. At birth, it's roughly the size of a chickpea, growing to the size of a cherry in the first week. By four weeks, her tummy will be the size of a walnut, and it remains much the same until she is six months old, when, in most cases, her tummy will be the size of her fist.

the art of breastfeeding

Breastfeeding offers a magical opportunity to develop a close, **intimate bond with your new baby**, and gives him the best possible start to life. Your breast milk provides all of the ingredients he needs for **optimum health, growth, and development**, and has plenty of benefits for you, too.

Q What are the advantages of breastfeeding?

A Breast milk provides a perfect start for your baby, affecting health and development on many different levels. For one thing, the composition of breast milk changes constantly, to allow for your baby's individual growth and changing nutritional needs. Research has found that breastfed babies have fewer incidences of vomiting, diarrhoea, gastroenteritis, as well as other infections and illnesses (it is especially important for premature babies to be breastfed as it strengthens their immune system). Breast milk also reduces the risk of chronic constipation, colic and other tummy disorders, and promotes growth. There is a reduced risk of childhood diabetes in breastfed babies, and they are considerably less likely to become obese or develop heart disease in later life. Research suggests breastfeeding exclusively for six months may protect against allergies, asthma, and eczema. There is also a reduced risk of SIDS (sudden infant death syndrome): research has found that of every 87 deaths from SIDS, only 3 took place in breastfed babies. The emotional benefits are well-documented – breastfed babies enjoy a warm, bonding, and emotional relationship with their mothers. Finally, breast milk is convenient – it's sterile, needs no preparation, and it's free.

★ did you know ...

that breastfeeding has benefits for you too? Women who breastfeed reduce their risk of developing breast, uterine, and ovarian cancers – by as much as 25 per cent for breast cancer. The risk of osteo-porosis and rheumatoid arthritis is reduced significantly too. It is also easier to shift pregnancy weight as breastfeeding burns on average 300–500 calories a day.

Q Should I be demand-feeding my baby?

A In the early days it's a good idea to feed as often as your baby wants, simply because your body has to adjust the amount of milk produced to ensure that your baby gets what he needs. After a few weeks, you can choose to continue to feed upon demand, or set up a routine. There are benefits for both approaches, and you'll need to decide what works best for you.

Some childcare experts believe that feeding on demand prevents any problems with milk supply, and also encourages emotional security, because you are meeting your baby's needs as and when he needs you to – teaching him trust. It is also now believed that babies who are fed when they are hungry learn to recognise hunger "cues", and develop a habit of eating to these cues, which is an important step in preventing obesity.

Some women, however, prefer to feed babies according to the clock – often every three or four hours. When babies cry between feeds, they are soothed, but not with milk. This can make life easier, knowing when you'll be sitting down for a feed, and when you have a little more time. Some women don't enjoy breastfeeding in public, and this approach means that you can schedule trips between feeds.

There's no reason, however, why you can't adapt things to include a little of both approaches. For example, you may wish to feed on demand throughout the day, and then wake your baby before you go to bed to fill up his tummy, and give you a little more sleep. You may also want to feed before setting out on a long journey, or to fall in with a family routine. That doesn't mean you are ignoring his requests for food, but that you are rescheduling the feeds a little to avoid having to breastfeed at times that are less convenient.

★ brainy babies

Breastfed infants develop higher IQs, and have improved brain and nervous system development – to the extent that breastfeeding is considered by many as the fourth trimester. Also, the way babies suck on the breast promotes development of facial structure, enhancing speech.

Q How will I know if my baby is getting enough milk?

A This is a concern that plagues many new mums. Unlike the contents of a bottle, breasts do not supply a "set" amount of milk per feed and do, in fact, adapt constantly to provide your baby with exactly the right amount she needs, according to her demands. There is an element of trust necessary here – believing that your baby is getting what she needs. If your baby is a healthy colour, putting on weight, alert and looking around when she is awake, and has regular wet and dirty nappies, she'll be getting enough. If, after losing a little weight in the first few days, which is entirely normal, your baby puts on weight slowly but surely, all is well. Breastfed babies do tend to gain weight more slowly than their bottle-fed peers, but this is simply a natural process. A health visitor will plot your baby's growth on centile charts in her Child Health Record book – talk to her if you're worried.

Q Will it confuse my baby to have a bottle from time to time?

A Many breastfeeding experts believe that offering a bottle will cause "nipple confusion", mainly because different types of sucking are involved. Sucking from a bottle requires less effort from babies, and they can quite easily become accustomed to getting milk more quickly and efficiently. However, if you can establish a successful pattern of breastfeeding over the first six weeks, your baby will develop the skills he needs to continue, and shouldn't find it too daunting to switch back and forth. In order to keep up the supply, which is based on your baby's demands, it's a good idea to avoid supplementing with formula milk too often.

Q Is it OK to drink a little alcohol if I'm breastfeeding?

A Alcohol enters your milk in much the same way that it does your bloodstream. Within about 20 minutes of drinking, it will appear in your milk. If you are feeling tipsy, you can expect your baby to feel pretty much the same. If you do want a couple of drinks, it's best to have them after you've breastfed, giving your body a chance to clear the alcohol before the next feed. No more than one or two units a week is recommended for breastfeeding mums.

Q Is it necessary to feed from both breasts during every feed?

A The most important thing is to ensure that your baby gets both types of milk produced by your breasts – the thirst-quenching foremilk, and the more calorific and nutritious hind milk. If your baby flits from one breast to the other, without emptying either, she may not be getting enough of the latter. In the early weeks, before the demand for your milk has been established by your baby, your breasts will overproduce quite substantially. A little baby may well be full after emptying the contents of one breast, in which case, it's fine to stop. However, do move her on to the other breast for your next feed, to avoid becoming engorged, and to ensure that your body begins to make the correct amount of milk to meet your baby's needs. Within a few weeks you should be producing the right amount for your baby, and she will be able to manage both breasts in a sitting.

Q How long should my baby feed on each breast?

A It's obviously difficult to work out whether your baby has actually managed to get both fore- and hind milk, because you can't see what is going on. A good feed normally lasts about 20 to 30 minutes. If he's "snacking", falling asleep on the breast, or losing concentration and looking around instead, he probably isn't getting all of what he needs. It may well be that he isn't particularly hungry, and you'll be better off trying again later. If you are demand breastfeeding, which means feeding your baby when he is hungry rather than to a set schedule (see page 25), you might need to urge him to finish a feed properly, or return to the same breast until he has emptied it.

Q If there are allergies in my family, is it advisable to breastfeed?

A Unfortunately, if there is allergy (such as asthma, eczema, hayfever or food allergies) in the family, the likelihood of a baby being "atopic" (the inherited predisposition to allergies) is very high. A huge amount of research has looked at ways of minimizing the potential for "high risk" babies to develop allergies in later life, but very few factors have been shown to make any difference at all. However, there is good evidence that exclusive breastfeeding can help. Current advice is to aim to breastfeed exclusively for six months, although it seems that it is the first four months that have the biggest impact in preventing food allergies and eczema. If there is a strong family history of allergy and you aren't able to breastfeed exclusively for this long, talk to your GP, who may recommend that you try a special hypoallergenic milk formula.

Q Should I wake my baby for a late night feed before I go to bed?

A Personally, I think it's OK to wake your baby. If you don't get much rest, you may find it hard to be a good mother. I think there is more chance of your baby starting to sleep through to a civilized hour if woken and fed just before you go to bed.

Q How long will expressed milk last?

A Expressed milk will last for about four hours at room temperature and, if you refrigerate it immediately after expressing, between 24 and 48 hours. If you are taking expressed milk out with you, keep it in a cool bag with ice packs, and it should last 24 hours or so.

★ sterilizing bottles

It's impossible to create a germ-free environment for your baby. However, warm milk is a perfect breeding ground for germs, so it's important to sterilize the bottles and teats you use for expressed milk. In the first year, your baby will be at her most vulnerable to germs, and carefully washing bottles will not be enough.

Q Can I continue to breastfeed when I return to work?

A If you have access to a breast pump at work, it may be possible to breastfeed exclusively (you'll need to refrigerate the milk and keep it at the same, cool, temperature while you transport it home). Before you return to work, you can freeze a supply of milk – it will last about three months. You'll obviously need to top up this supply. If you're able to feed your baby before you go to work, immediately upon your return, and perhaps again before bedtime or during the night, it is perfectly possible to breastfeed exclusively.

Some mothers who breastfeed part-time, alongside bottle-feeding, find that their babies are reluctant to go back to the breast. However, if you can manage to offer the same feeds each day – perhaps morning and evening – your baby will get used to the routine. Your breasts will also begin to produce milk at the appropriate time.

a new mum's diet

As a new mum, you'll need to make sure that you get plenty of fresh, wholesome food to **keep your energy levels high.** Eating well also helps to ensure that your breastfed baby will have a constant supply of good-quality milk to **keep him healthy and satisfied.**

Q How many calories do I need when I'm breastfeeding?

A Most women need at least 2, 200 calories per day to maintain a supply of good-quality milk, but if you are active, over- or underweight, your needs may be different. Exclusive breastfeeding burns around 300–500 calories per day, and in most cases these need to be replaced. But listen to your body – some days you may need to eat more.

Q Is it OK to diet while breastfeeding?

A This is never a good idea; you need a balanced diet and adequate calories to produce enough good-quality milk for your baby. Also, toxins are stored in fat cells in your body, and when you diet, these are released into your bloodstream and into your milk, eventually reaching your baby. While breastfeeding, you can lose weight healthily (about 2kg/5lb a month) by eating plenty of fresh, whole foods and giving up refined goodies.

Q Which foods should I try to include in my diet while breastfeeding and why?

A A balanced diet will help to ensure that your baby gets the nutrients she needs from your milk, and that you stay healthy, relaxed, and full of energy.

Aim for a diet that is high in unrefined carbohydrates (wholegrain breads, pastas, cereals, brown rice, and grains), which will provide you with sustainable energy and fibre to encourage healthy digestion. Pulses, such as beans, peas, and chickpeas, are an excellent source of healthy unrefined carbs, fibre, vitamins, minerals, and protein. Lentils and chickpeas, in particular, are rich in iron, which can be low in breastfeeding mums. You'll also find iron in dried fruit, fish, and leafy greens, but red meat has the best and most easily absorbed form. Essential fatty acids, found in oily fish, nuts, and seeds, encourage optimum health for you, but they'll also help to ensure that your baby grows and develops properly – in particular, her brain and nervous system. Fresh vegetables and fruit are essential for the vitamins, minerals, and fibre they offer. Finally, aim for four servings of calcium – found in dairy produce, soya, and leafy greens – and three or four servings of protein a day (in lean meats, fish, pulses, eggs, seeds, nuts, and soya).

Q Are there any foods I should avoid while breastfeeding?

A Breast milk is a sweet, nutritious food that takes on the flavours of the foods you are eating, giving your baby her first tastes of food. There are no foods that need to be avoided, but keep an eye out for those that may cause her discomfort. If she appears to be uncomfortable after feeds, crying, vomiting, drawing her knees up to her chest, or experiencing "wind", it may well be that something you have eaten doesn't agree with her. Removing the offending food should make a difference instantly.

Many believe that the foods in a breastfeeding mum's diet can cause colic. Although no-one is exactly sure what causes colic, as the symptoms and causes differ between babies, lots of mums swear by cutting out the "wind-producing" foods, such as cabbage, onions, garlic, and Brussels sprouts.

All studies suggest that what you eat while breastfeeding makes no difference to later allergic disease, including food allergies. However, official advice in the UK and US is that mothers may wish to avoid peanuts during pregnancy and breast-feeding, and to avoid giving infants peanuts for the first three years of their life. This remains contentious and is under review.

Q I find breastfeeding very draining; is there something that I should be eating to lift my energy levels?

A Look at the type of carbohydrates you are eating. If they are mostly "quick-release", you'll experience a surge of energy, followed by a slump that will leave you feeling weary and drained. So go for slow-release carbs, such as wholegrains, pulses, seeds, nuts, and dried fruit, and if you do have unrefined foods in your diet, such as white rice, bread or pasta, cakes, and biscuits, eat them with a little protein to slow down their transit into your blood stream. An egg on white toast, or some cheese on pasta, can make all the difference. Make sure you are getting plenty of iron too. Iron-deficiency anaemia is common in pregnancy and during the postnatal period, and can leave you feeling exhausted. It can help to drink a little fruit juice with iron-rich foods, to encourage their absorption. If all else fails, see your doctor.

★ did you know...

that when you're breastfeeding you need to make sure you drink between 2.5 and 3 litres (4 ½–5 pints), or 8 to 12 glasses of fluids a day? Breastfeeding requires a lot of liquid and if you become dehydrated you'll feel tired and probably irritable or tearful too. It's a good idea to have some water or fresh fruit juice by your side before you settle down to breastfeed. See my refreshing Infused water recipes on page 49 to help quench your thirst.

PREPARATION 15 MINUTES | COOKING TIME 30 MINUTES | MAKES 8 BARS

granola bars

Flax seeds (also called linseed) are extremely rich in **omega-3 oils,** similar to the type found in salmon and other oily fish. Wheatgerm contains a lot of **folate and vitamin E.** They both have a slightly nutty taste, which helps to make these oat bars **extra delicious.**

110g (4oz) rolled oats

45g (1½oz) sunflower seeds

55g (2oz) pecan nuts, roughly chopped

30g (1oz) wheatgerm

55g (2oz) raisins

55g (2oz) dried cranberries

30g (1oz) flax seeds

170g (6oz) golden syrup or clear honey

55g (2oz) soft light brown sugar

55g (2oz) butter, plus extra
for greasing

1 tsp pure vanilla extract

½ tsp salt

1 Preheat the oven to 150°C (130°C fan), gas 2. Lightly grease a 28 x 19cm (11 x 7½in) cake tin with butter, and line the bottom and sides of the tin with baking parchment. Set aside.

2 Mix the oats, sunflower seeds, pecans, wheatgerm, raisins, cranberries, and flax seeds together in a large bowl. Put the syrup, sugar, and butter in a saucepan and warm gently until the butter has melted and the sugar has dissolved. Remove from the heat and stir in the vanilla extract and salt, then pour over the oat mixture. Stir with a wooden spoon until everything is well combined. Press firmly into the cake tin (a potato masher is good for this).

3 Bake for 30 minutes until the centre is just firm (if using honey you may need to bake for an extra 5 minutes). Remove from the oven and allow to cool for 15 minutes, then mark into bars with a sharp knife. Leave to cool completely before removing the bars from the tin. Store in the refrigerator.

PREPARATION 15 MINUTES | COOKING TIME 15 MINUTES | MAKES 2 PORTIONS

baked cod gratin

This dish uses a very **simple cheese sauce** that can easily be made while the fish is cooking. However, **you can substitute** a good-quality **ready-made cheese sauce**, if you prefer.

250g (9oz) baby leaf spinach, carefully washed

Salt and pepper

15g (½oz) butter

2 x 140g (5oz) pieces of skinless cod fillet, about 1cm (½in) thick

1 heaped tbsp cornflour

150ml (5fl oz) milk

30g (1oz) Gruyère or mature Cheddar cheese, grated

3 tbsp freshly grated Parmesan cheese

1 egg yolk

¼ tsp Dijon mustard

Pinch of paprika or cayenne pepper

1 Preheat the oven to 220°C (200°C fan), gas 7. Preheat the grill to high. Heat 2 tbsp water in a large saucepan over a high heat. Add the spinach and cover. Cook for 2–3 minutes. Transfer the spinach to a colander and squeeze out as much water as possible by pressing with a wooden spoon. Season to taste.

2 Lightly butter a small ovenproof dish using half of the butter. Arrange the spinach in the bottom of the dish. Season the cod and sit the fillets on the spinach. Dot with remaining butter. Bake for 10 minutes or until the fish is just opaque all the way through.

3 Mix the cornflour and 2 tbsp of milk to a paste, and add to the remaining milk in a saucepan. Bring to the boil, whisking for about 4 minutes until thickened. Add the Gruyère and 1 tbsp Parmesan and stir until the cheese has melted. Stir in the egg yolk and mustard. Season with salt, pepper, and paprika or cayenne.

4 Remove the dish from the oven and spoon the sauce over the fish and spinach. Sprinkle with the remaining Parmesan. Grill for 2–3 minutes until the sauce is lightly browned and bubbling.

PREPARATION 15-20 MINUTES | COOKING TIME 30-45 MINUTES | MAKES 4 PORTIONS

sweet root soup

Soups can make **a satisfying lunch** or snack and are useful to have in the fridge to heat up quickly if you feel hungry. Carrots, sweet potatoes, and squash all have **high levels of beta-carotene,** a powerful antioxidant.

1 tbsp olive oil

1 medium red onion, chopped

2 carrots, peeled and diced

1 small sweet potato, peeled and diced (250g/9oz)

½ small butternut squash, peeled and diced (150g/5½oz peeled weight)

1 tsp mild curry paste

1 tsp clear honey

600ml (1 pint) vegetable stock

Salt and pepper

Crème fraîche, to serve (optional)

Fresh coriander leaves, to garnish (optional)

1 Heat the oil in a large pan and sauté the vegetables for 10–15 minutes until turning soft. Stir in the curry paste and honey, and cook for 1 minute. Add the stock and bring up to a simmer, then cook uncovered for 20–25 minutes until the vegetables are tender.

3 Allow to cool slightly before blending until smooth (be careful when blending hot liquids). Season to taste. Warm gently before serving. This is particularly nice if you top each bowl of soup with a small spoonful of crème fraîche and a few coriander leaves.

PREPARATION 10-15 MINUTES | COOKING TIME 15 MINUTES | MAKES 2 PORTIONS

bag-baked salmon

Oily fish such as salmon contains plenty of **omega-3 fatty acids,** which are **good for both you and your baby.** These bags of baked salmon can be assembled earlier in the day and then **stored in the refrigerator** until needed.

¼ red pepper, thinly sliced

2 fresh shiitake or oyster mushrooms, stalks removed and thinly sliced

2 x 170g (6oz) pieces of salmon fillet, about 2.5cm (1in) thick

2 large spring onions, thinly sliced

½ tsp grated fresh root ginger

2 tsp soy sauce

1 tbsp mirin

½ tsp caster sugar

1   Preheat the oven to 200°C (180°C fan), gas 6. Cut out two rectangles of foil about 40 x 30cm (16 x 12in), and two of baking parchment the same size.

2   Lay the foil rectangles on a flat surface and put a piece of baking parchment on top of each. Mix the red pepper and mushrooms together and spoon half into the centre of each piece of parchment. Sit the salmon on top of the vegetables and scatter on the spring onions. Mix together the ginger, soy sauce, mirin, and sugar until the sugar has dissolved, then carefully spoon over the salmon.

3   Bring the long sides of the foil and parchment together over the salmon and roll and fold over to seal. Twist and scrunch the ends together so that the salmon is completely enclosed. Set the bags on a baking tray and bake for about 15 minutes until the salmon is opaque all the way through and flakes when pressed with a fork. Undo the parcels and transfer the salmon to a plate, then spoon over the vegetables and sauce.

PREPARATION 10 MINUTES, PLUS 1 HOUR MARINATING | COOKING TIME 10 MINUTES | MAKES 2 PORTIONS

seared tuna with coriander couscous

Tuna and other oily fish are the **best sources of omega-3** essential **fatty acids**, which are very important for the development of a baby's eyesight and brain (**a baby's brain triples in size** in the first year). It is thought that omega-3s can pass to your baby through your breast milk. So try to eat **two portions of oily fish a week.**

2 tbsp soy sauce

2 tbsp mirin

1 tbsp soft light brown sugar

1 x 225g (8oz) fresh tuna steak, about 1.5cm (⅝in) thick

1 tbsp sunflower oil

Couscous

125g (4½oz) couscous

1 tbsp olive oil

200ml (7fl oz) hot vegetable stock

2 spring onions, thinly sliced

Handful of fresh coriander leaves, roughly chopped

1 tbsp lime juice (or to taste)

Salt and pepper

1 Mix the soy sauce, mirin, and sugar together in a large dish. Add the tuna and leave to marinate in the fridge for no more than 1 hour, turning the tuna over halfway through.

2 Put the couscous in a large bowl and stir in the olive oil and the hot stock. Cover the bowl with cling film and leave to stand for 5 minutes. Uncover and fluff up the couscous with a fork. Stir in the spring onions, coriander, and lime juice. Season, then spread out on two plates.

3 Put a ridged grill pan over a high heat and brush with sunflower oil. Remove the tuna from the marinade (reserve the marinade) and pat dry with kitchen paper. Sear for 2 minutes on each side for medium-cooked tuna (thinner pieces will cook more quickly). Rest the tuna on a plate for 5 minutes.

4 Put the reserved marinade in a saucepan with 2 tbsp water. Bring to the boil for 1 minute to make a sauce. Slice the tuna and lay it on the couscous, then drizzle over the sauce.

PREPARATION 10 MINUTES | COOKING TIME 8–10 MINUTES | MAKES 2 PORTIONS

pasta with rocket and mascarpone sauce

This sauce is so quick that you can make it while the pasta is cooking. If you like garlic then **add a small clove** to the food processor **with the rocket**. You can also toss in a handful of cherry tomatoes (halved) at the end for a bit of **bright colour contrast**.

225g (8oz) pasta bows, spirals,
  or corkscrews

110g (4oz) wild rocket (4 handfuls)

125g (4½oz) mascarpone (half of
  a 250g tub)

4 tbsp freshly grated Parmesan cheese,
  plus extra to serve

2 tsp lemon juice

Salt and pepper

1 Cook the pasta according to the packet instructions. Meanwhile, put the rocket in the bowl of a food processor and whiz until finely chopped. Add the mascarpone, Parmesan, and lemon juice, and whiz again to combine (if the mascarpone is very thick and creamy, you might need to add 1 tbsp milk). Season to taste with salt and pepper.

2 Drain the pasta well and return to the pan. Add the rocket sauce and toss to coat the pasta. Serve with extra Parmesan.

PREPARATION 20 MINUTES | COOKING TIME 25 MINUTES | MAKES 4–6 PORTIONS

frittata provençale

I may be mixing my countries a bit in the title here, but **a flat omelette** bolstered with **summer vegetables** makes a lovely quick lunch or **light supper**. This is also good cold, so keep leftovers in the fridge for a time **when you need a quick snack.**

3–4 new potatoes

6 eggs

1 tsp chopped fresh thyme leaves (or other herbs such as chives, parsley, tarragon, and chervil)

4 tbsp crème fraîche or double cream

Salt and pepper

2 tbsp olive oil

1 small red onion, thinly sliced

½ red pepper, thinly sliced

1 medium courgette, thinly sliced

1 clove garlic, crushed

110g (4oz) Gruyère cheese, grated

2 tbsp freshly grated Parmesan cheese

1 Cook the potatoes in boiling salted water for about 12 minutes until just tender. When cool, cut into slices and set aside. Beat the eggs in a jug with the thyme and crème fraîche. Season well and set aside.

2 Heat the oil in a medium non-stick frying pan (20–23cm/8–9in) and sauté the onion, red pepper, and courgette for 8–10 minutes until just soft. Add the garlic and potatoes, and cook for a further minute. Spread out the vegetables in the pan, then pour in the eggs. Cook for 2–3 minutes, stirring occasionally. Leave to cook for a further 6–7 minutes until the frittata is just set underneath, but still wobbly on top. Meanwhile, preheat the grill to high.

3 Scatter the cheeses over the frittata and grill for 2–4 minutes until the cheese is golden and bubbly and the frittata has set on top. Remove from the grill and leave to stand for 5 minutes.

4 Loosen the frittata from the pan using a spatula, then slide out on to a large plate. Cut into wedges to serve.

PREPARATION 10 MINUTES | MAKES 2 PORTIONS

southwestern salad

Sweetcorn and beans contain complementary **amino acids**, which means that when they are combined they are a great source of protein. Corn is also rich in folate. **Crunchy salads** tossed in **tangy dressings** are popular in southern California and the southwestern states of the USA.

2 tbsp mayonnaise (reduced fat is fine)

2 tbsp natural yogurt

1 tsp lemon juice

1–2 tbsp milk

2 tsp chopped fresh dill or coriander

Salt and pepper

1 x 198g tin sweetcorn, drained

½ x 410g tin kidney beans, drained and rinsed

½ red pepper, diced

2 spring onions, thinly sliced

¼ iceberg or ½ romaine lettuce

1 avocado, sliced

1 In a large bowl whisk together the mayonnaise, yogurt, and lemon juice. Whisk in enough milk to give a coating consistency, then stir in the dill and season with salt and pepper. Add the sweetcorn, beans, red pepper, and spring onions, and toss to coat in the dressing. Cover and chill until needed.

2 Just before serving, put the lettuce in the bottom of a salad bowl and spoon the tossed salad on top, then scatter over the avocado slices.

PREPARATION TIME 10 MINUTES PLUS CHILLING | COOKING TIME 30–35 MINUTES | SERVES 2–4 ADULTS

chicken, avocado, and brown rice salad

Eating a combination of protein and whole grains at mealtimes is **a good way to satisfy hunger pangs** and boost energy levels. I love the nuttiness of brown rice in this salad, but you could also use the **wonderful quinoa grain** from Peru. Cook according to the packet instructions.

2 litres (3½ pints) vegetable stock

225g (8oz) brown rice

4 tbsp olive oil

2 tbsp lemon juice

Salt and pepper

1 bunch of spring onions, thinly sliced

55g (2oz) pine nuts, toasted

Handful of fresh coriander leaves, roughly chopped

1 avocado, skin and stone removed, then thinly sliced

2 cooked chicken breasts, thinly sliced

1 Bring the stock to the boil in a large saucepan. Add the rice and stir. Bring back to the boil, then reduce the heat, cover, and cook for 30–35 minutes until the rice is tender and has absorbed all the liquid. Cool and chill until needed (the rice can be cooked up to 24 hours in advance).

2 When ready to serve, whisk together the olive oil and lemon juice with salt and pepper to taste. Stir this dressing into the rice together with the spring onions, pine nuts, and coriander. Top the salad with the avocado and chicken, and serve.

PREPARATION TIME 10 MINUTES | COOKING TIME 9 MINUTES | SERVES 4 ADULTS

annabel's salmon stir-fry with noodles

It's good to eat oily fish like salmon when you are breastfeeding as the **essential fatty acids** are very important for your baby's brain development. In this quick and easy stir-fry, **the vegetables are lightly cooked** to preserve their nutrients, and you can vary them to your own likes and dislikes.

2 tbsp sunflower oil

1 carrot, cut into matchsticks

1 bunch of spring onions, cut diagonally in short lengths

125g (4½oz) broccoli, cut in tiny florets

125g (4½oz) baby sweetcorn, cut in chunks

125g (4½oz) sugar snap peas

450g (1lb) salmon fillet, skinned and cut into 2cm (¾in) cubes

385g (13½oz) pack straight-to-wok noodles

Sauce

2 tbsp plum sauce

2 tbsp hoisin sauce

4 tbsp soy sauce

4 tbsp sake or dry sherry

1tsp toasted sesame oil

1 Mix together the sauce ingredients and set aside.

2 Heat the sunflower oil in a wok or large frying pan. Stir-fry the carrot, spring onions, and broccoli for 2 minutes. Add the sweetcorn and sugarsnap peas and stir-fry for a further 3 minutes.

3 Add the salmon and stir-fry until it it cooked through, about 2 minutes. Add the noodles. Pour over the sauce, toss gently for about 2 minutes until everything is coated in the sauce and the noodles are hot through. Serve in warm bowls.

PREPARATION TIME 5 MINUTES | COOKING TIME 4–5 MINUTES | SERVES 1 ADULT

chicken quesadilla

Quesadillas are quick and tasty, perfect **when you are hungry** and tired, and want an **end-of-the-day snack** without any fuss.

2 flour tortillas (wraps)

2 tbsp salsa

55g (2oz) cooked chicken breast, shredded

30g (1oz) Cheddar cheese, grated

To serve

1 tbsp soured cream (optional)

2 tbsp guacamole or a few avocado slices (optional)

1 Place a large, non-stick frying pan over a medium heat to warm up.

2 Put one tortilla on a plate and spread over the salsa. Scatter the chicken and cheese evenly over the tortilla, and top with the second tortilla. Slide into the hot frying pan and lower the heat slightly. Cook for about 2 minutes or until the underside is toasted, pressing the quesadilla down lightly with a fish slice or spatula.

3 Using your hand to steady the top, carefully flip over the quesadilla with a fish slice or spatula. Cook for a further 2–3 minutes until the second side is toasted, pressing down lightly. When the quesadilla is ready, the cheese will have melted and the chicken will be hot through. (If flipping the quesadilla makes you nervous, you can pop the frying pan under a preheated grill to toast the top.)

4 Slide the quesadilla on to a plate and leave to stand for 1–2 minutes, then cut in quarters. Serve with soured cream and guacamole or avocado slices, if you like.

PREPARATION TIME 10 MINUTES | COOKING TIME 13–17 MINUTES | SERVES 2 ADULTS

beef, mushroom, and spinach stir-fry

Here is a recipe to **boost your iron levels**. Beef and spinach are both high in iron and make a quick and tasty stir-fry. If you put the rice or pasta on to cook before you start stir-frying, dinner will be **on the table in less than 30 minutes.**

2 tbsp sunflower oil

1 onion, halved and thinly sliced

1 garlic clove, crushed

175g (6oz) chestnut mushrooms, thinly sliced

225g (8oz) fillet or sirloin steak, trimmed and cut in thin strips

85g (3oz) baby spinach leaves, washed and dried

150ml (5fl oz) beef stock

1 tbsp oyster sauce

1 tsp soft light brown sugar

1 tsp cornflour

2 tsp water

1 tbsp soy sauce or to taste

To serve

115g (4oz) rice or fusilli pasta, cooked according to packet directions

1 spring onion, shredded (optional)

1 Heat half the oil in a wok or large frying pan, add the onion, and stir-fry for 4–5 minutes until starting to brown. Add the garlic and mushrooms to the wok and stir-fry for another 4–5 minutes until the mushrooms have cooked through and are turning golden at the edges. Spoon the mushrooms and onions into a bowl and set aside.

2 Heat the remaining oil in the wok. Add the steak and stir-fry for 2–3 minutes until browned. Add the spinach and cook for 1–2 minutes until it has wilted, then return the cooked mushrooms and onions to the wok. Add the stock, oyster sauce, sugar, and cornflour blended with the water. Bring to the boil, stirring constantly. Simmer for 1–2 minutes until the sauce has thickened.

3 Add the soy sauce, then taste and add a little more, if you like. Serve spooned over rice or pasta, garnished with the spring onion, if using.

PREPARATION TIME 5 MINUTES PLUS CHILLING | MAKES 1.5 LITRES (2¾ PINTS)

infused waters

It is important to **drink plenty of fluids** when breastfeeding, but try to avoid sugar-filled fizzy drinks and caffeine. Posh health spas serve infused waters, **which are refreshing**, and a lot more interesting than plain water. Why not make your own, and refrigerate until needed?

lime, cucumber, and mint

1 lime, thinly sliced

7.5cm (3in) piece cucumber, peeled, halved lengthways, and finely sliced

2 large sprigs of fresh mint

1.5 litres (2¾ pints) water

1 Put the lime, cucumber, mint, and water in a large jug (or divide between two smaller jugs).

2 Cover and chill overnight. Stir before serving.

citrus refresher

1 lemon, thinly sliced

1 lime, thinly sliced

1 orange, thinly sliced

1.5 litres (2¾ pints) water

1 Put the sliced fruit and water in a large jug (or divide between two smaller jugs).

2 Cover and chill overnight. Stir before serving.

all about bottle-feeding

Not everyone finds it easy or possible to breastfeed, but you can be confident that **formula milk offers your baby** the nutrients that will encourage optimum health and development. Bottle-feeding also gives **dad and other members of the family** a chance to experience the wonders of feeding a new baby.

Q **Is there anything I can do to encourage bonding if I'm bottle-feeding?**

A Making the experience of being fed pleasurable and nurturing is important whether you are breastfeeding or bottle-feeding, and physical comfort is the most important element of this.

Hold your baby close to you and let her know that she's safe and secure in your arms. Keep her pressed close to your chest, so that she can hear your heartbeat, smell you, and feel comforted. Talk quietly to her, or sing, so that she can hear your voice, and be reassured that you are there for her. Look into her eyes, stroke her face, and encourage her to do the same in return. Babies love to be cuddled and held, and skin-to-skin contact is also recommended from time to time, which mimics the breastfeeding experience. A good routine also helps, so your baby knows what to expect and looks forward to this positive experience.

Q **What should I look for in a formula?**

A The truth is that most formulas are pretty much the same. All now contain essential fatty acids (EFAs), which are essential for your baby's healthy growth and development – in particular, the development of her brain and nervous system. Others also offer probiotics, a substance that promotes the growth of good bacteria in your baby's gut.

Like all milks, breast milk contains two types of protein: whey and casein. The balance in breast milk is in favour of whey (70 per cent whey and 30 per cent casein). It is a good idea, therefore, to look for a formula with a similar ratio. Formulas that have more casein tend to be harder for your baby to digest, and are more suited to the older infant.

There may be other claims made on your baby's formula packet, such as additional immune-boosting nutrients, etc; however, it's worth noting that baby formula manufacturing is very, very closely monitored, and nothing can be added without going through rigorous scrutiny by government health authorities. For this reason, there will be little difference between formulas – once one brand has an extra ingredient, the others soon follow suit.

Q Is there any advantage to buying pre-mixed formulas?

A The main advantage to pre-mixed formulas is their convenience. They can be carried with you wherever you go, and used on the spot, with no mixing or preparation. This is particularly useful when travelling, as you may not have the equipment you need to prepare feeds, nor any way to sterilize the implements. Many parents find it useful to use pre-mixed formulas at home, too – mainly because they take the hard work out of bottle-feeding, and there is no concern about the formula being inaccurately measured (see box, below). The disadvantage, however, is that they are expensive.

Q Can I use mineral water when preparing my baby's formula?

A Mineral water is not recommended in the preparation of formula, because it is designed for adults and not babies, and contains (not surprisingly) minerals, including salt, which your baby does not need. There will be the correct balance of minerals in your baby's formula, and adding additional ones in the form of mineral water can upset the balance. Bottled spring water is fine, as it has a lower concentration of minerals.

Q Are there particular types of bottles or teats that are easier for a baby to manage?

A Narrow-necked bottles tend to be more versatile, because they will take most teats designed for this type of bottle. Silicone teats tend to be more expensive, but they are more durable and will last longer. Latex teats can, however, be softer than silicone, which makes it easier for some babies to suck (particularly if they have a weak suck).

Choose a teat that is the right size for the age of your baby, and experiment a little to see if he prefers faster or slow-flow teats. Most babies will finish a bottle in no more than 20 minutes, so if it is taking longer, consider switching to a faster teat. If he's finishing a bottle in less than 10 minutes, switch to a slower one.

I've found that some babies, particularly those who have started out being breastfed, seem to prefer the teats that are shaped more like a nipple, with a wide, flat base, and a "nipple-shaped" centre.

★ did you know ...
that it is very important to follow the manufacturer's instructions when making up formula milk? This may seem fiddly at first, but it will soon become second nature. Formula milk is perfectly balanced to ensure that it is easily digestible, and meets your baby's needs. Too much of the powder or liquid can cause your baby to become constipated, or thirsty; too little may mean she isn't getting the nutrition she needs.

time for the first taste?

The first months of your baby's life may fly by, and as **the gaps between feeds lengthen**, and he becomes more alert and expends more energy, you may find that he is **showing signs of being ready** for solid food. Let your baby take the lead.

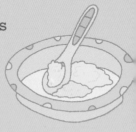

Q My four-month-old seems hungry all the time – could she be ready to begin solids?

A Currently the most common recommendation for weaning age comes from the World Health Organization (WHO), which suggests waiting until six months of age to introduce solids. We know, however, that babies' digestive and immune systems can tolerate food a little earlier (from around 17 weeks of age), and so the exact timing is really dependent on your baby. Every baby is different, so you need to assess her development before weaning. If she is demanding feeds more often, shows an interest in the food you are eating (for example reaching out for food on your plate), and is "mouthing" (chewing on her knuckles or putting her fingers in her mouth), it is likely that she's ready. Speak to your health visitor if you think this is the case. Suitable early weaning foods include vegetables, fruit, and cereals.

Q Why do experts now recommend waiting until six months to wean?

A All countries, and health experts, have adopted the guidelines from the WHO, which recommends exclusive breastfeeding until six months. This is particularly important in underdeveloped countries, where breast milk is sterile and the safest feeding option, and is also a good safeguard for children who may have a poor weaning diet.

The main reason to wait until six months is that until this time your breast milk will provide your baby with everything he needs to grow and develop; however, after this, breast milk alone provides insufficient essential nutrients, like iron and vitamin D. That's not to say that breast milk has no nutritional value after this time (see page 57), but your baby's growth and development demands more nutrients that need to be provided through weaning foods. Similarly, formula-fed infants also need to be weaned at six months, to supplement nutritional intake. If your baby does show signs that he is ready for solid food a little earlier (see left), it's a good idea to speak to your health visitor about the possibility of introducing some simple foods, as these will ensure normal oral motor skill development in your baby (i.e. sucking and chewing).

Q Will early weaning make my baby more prone to allergies?

A Another argument that is sometimes put forward against weaning babies earlier than six months is based on the notion that early weaning makes babies more prone to allergies. However, this is not true. Most babies' digestive systems can tolerate basic food from around 17 weeks, and there is no evidence that delaying weaning beyond this time prevents allergies in either allergic or non-allergic infants.

Q Does my baby need juice or water alongside her milk feeds?

A Breastfed babies do not need water or juice, as your milk is perfectly balanced, both to quench thirst and to keep her well hydrated. If she has a virus and is struggling to keep down her milk, you may need to offer water or oral rehydration solution to ensure that she does not become dehydrated, although the best advice is to continue breastfeeding, both to ensure she gets enough fluids, and to take advantage of the antibodies that your breast milk offers. Bottle-fed babies may need to have a little water alongside their feeds.

Baby juices are not necessary at this age, as your baby will be getting all the nutrients she needs from her milk. If she's thirsty and not interested in water, you could heavily dilute a little baby juice, but you may be making a rod for your own back, as she will be less likely to take plain water later on, if she's used to the sweetness of juice. If she is ill and there is risk of dehydration, however, any fluids, such as heavily diluted juice, water, and oral rehydration solution are appropriate.

Q My baby keeps reaching out for other people's food. Should I let him taste?

A Once again, from around five months onwards, small tastes of food are acceptable. Be aware, however, that your baby won't have developed the ability to chew, and won't for some time, so anything offered should be soft and, ideally, puréed. Remember to keep to foods that are suitable for your baby's age. Steer away from foods that contain flavourings, colourings, and sweeteners, and avoid anything with sugar and salt, as you'll want to encourage your little one to develop a taste for the natural sweetness of healthy foods such as fruit and vegetables, before a sweet tooth can be established.

 mastering a cup

Most babies drink from a cup at around four months, although you will have to hold it to his mouth and encourage him to sip. He should be able to do this himself at around six months, although some little ones may manage it sooner, and others a little later. Don't worry if your baby shows no interest. He should be getting adequate fluids from his milk feeds (and solids – if he's begun weaning). It may be easier to offer all drinks, apart from milk in a cup, to prevent him from developing the habit of taking everything from a bottle.

chapter 2

6–9 months:
ready for food

6–9 months:
what you can expect

Your baby's first spoonfuls are an exciting milestone for both you and your baby. It's only natural to **approach weaning** with some anxiety – there are lots of things to consider as your baby begins his journey on the road to independence, **but it's a process you'll both enjoy.**

Q How do I know if my baby is ready for solid foods?

A Your baby will start to show some interest in what you are eating, and perhaps reach out to taste it himself. He will probably be hungrier than usual, often unsatisfied after his normal milk feed, and possibly waking in the night for an extra feed, when he has previously slept through. He should be "mouthing" too – putting his fingers in his mouth or chewing on his knuckles.

It's worth noting that a growth spurt commonly occurs between three and four months of age, which may cause him to wake more frequently at night, and perhaps feed much more frequently (sometimes appearing to be non-stop!). This growth spurt accounts for his hunger, so don't assume he's ready for solids just yet!

Q Do I still need to breastfeed when I begin weaning?

A Your baby will need formula or breast milk until she is at least 12 months, when her diet is varied enough to offer the correct balance of nutrients. Weaning foods offer first tastes rather than proper nutrition, and as she gradually eats more, her milk feeds will be replaced by proper meals. Don't be tempted to give up the milk, though. Breastfeed as usual, or, if you are bottle-feeding, remember that she will need at least 500–600ml (about 1 pint) per day. If less than this is consumed, it's worth discussing with a doctor or health visitor, as she may need extra vitamins. Give her a milk feed first thing in the morning and at bedtime, and other milk feeds during the day. The timing will depend on the stage of weaning, but you should try to give milk feeds after meals and limit the amount of milk between meals.

Q Why should I make homemade purées for my baby?

A The healthiest baby foods are the ones you make yourself. You can be sure of using the best-quality ingredients with no thickeners or additives, including salt or sugar. The ingredients of most commercial baby foods are heated to a very high temperature and then cooled, to sterliize them – a process that destroys some nutrients. By using fresh ingredients, your homemade purées will be that much more nutritious.

Homemade purées taste much better too, and they're a great way to introduce your baby to the delights of fresh, whole foods, with their intrinsic sweetness and flavours. Put some time in now, and you'll reap the benefits later. Giving your baby homemade food will help to make the transition to family food much easier.

★ cheap, healthy food

Would you believe that parents in the UK fork out around £70 million every year on commercially prepared baby food? By making your own, you'll be saving money (even taking into consideration the time it takes for you to make them), and you'll be giving your child a great start in life.

beginning weaning

This time is **an important transition** for you and your baby. Whether she's a slow starter, or instant foodie, you'll both **take pleasure in the process** of mastering self-feeding, introducing new tastes, and **enjoying the world of food.**

Q Can I wait longer than six months to introduce first foods?

A It may be tempting to wait, given that your baby's digestive and immune systems will be that much more mature, but it doesn't help to do so.

For one thing, babies who start later often find it difficult to manage lumps, and may be more reluctant to try new tastes and textures. Also, if you wait to introduce fruit and vegetables, you'll delay moving on to protein-rich foods, such as oily fish, which contain essential fatty acids that are vital for your baby's development. Also, a baby's iron supply, inherited from his mother, runs out at six months, so it's important not to wait too long before introducing iron-rich foods such as red meat and lentils. With regards to food allergies, there is no evidence that delaying the introduction of allergenic foods (such as cow's milk, egg, wheat, fish, and soya) after the six-month mark makes your child less likely to have food allergies.

Q What is the best way to introduce solids to my baby?

A Firstly, don't worry about how much your baby is eating. The idea of first foods is to encourage your baby to experience new tastes and textures, and to get used to the idea of taking something from a spoon and swallowing it. While nutrition is important – meaning, simply, that everything you offer your baby should be fresh and nutritious – it's actually more important that she develops a taste for a variety of different foods.

It's perfectly fine to introduce new foods to your baby each day. If there is a history of allergy in the family, you may like to offer a new food every two or three days, so you can watch out for any signs of a reaction. Reactions that can indicate a potential problem include skin rashes, vomiting, diarrhoea, and even breathing difficulties.

To begin with, offer food halfway through a milk feed, so your baby isn't frantically hungry. At first, the purées need to be semi-liquid, and as much like milk in consistency as possible so that they are easy to swallow – add breast milk, formula, or a little water from the bottom of the steamer or saucepan, to thin the purée.

understanding allergies

Food allergies are on the increase, but still remain uncommon in little ones, and are very often outgrown. **It helps to be aware** of the symptoms, and to know where to turn. The best advice is not to panic, and to **talk to your doctor** if you have any concerns.

Q **How will I know if my baby has a food allergy?**

A Food allergies are much more common among children in families with a history of allergy. Babies who suffer from eczema are particularly at risk – and the more severe the eczema, the more likely there is to be a food allergy. Some food allergies are fairly easy to spot – as soon as the food is eaten, often for the first or second time, a reaction occurs (see box, right).

Delayed allergies may also be a problem for infants. In the past, these were sometimes called food intolerance, but this isn't the correct term, because an intolerance doesn't involve the immune system. Delayed allergic reactions do involve the immune system, but parts of it that take longer to respond. This means it can be difficult to pinpoint a particular food as the problem, as sufferers may continue to eat and drink it. Milk, soya, egg, and wheat are often the main culprits, and symptoms include eczema, reflux, colic, poor growth, diarrhoea and constipation. These get better only when the food is removed from the diet. However, all of these symptoms commonly occur during childhood and an allergy is only one possible explanation. You'll need the help of an experienced doctor to diagnose a food allergy.

★ **immediate food allergies**

Moderate symptoms

These typically affect the skin, the respiratory system, and the gut. Seek medical advice.

- A flushed face, hives, or a red and itchy rash around the mouth, tongue, or eyes. This can spread across the entire body
- Mild swelling, particularly of the lips, eyes, and face
- A runny or blocked nose, sneezing, and watering eyes
- Nausea, vomiting, tummy cramps, and diarrhoea
- A scratchy or itchy mouth and throat

Severe symptoms (anaphylaxis)

This an emergency – call 999.

- Wheezing or difficulty in breathing
- Swelling of the tongue and throat, restricting the airways. This can cause noisy breathing (especially on breathing in), a cough or a change in your baby's cry or voice
- Lethargy, floppiness, or collapse

mostly milk

Weaning can sometimes be overwhelming for your baby, and **he'll take comfort** in his regular milk feeds. What's more, the nutrients in his milk will support his **growth and development** while he gets to grips with the whole new world of **tastes and textures**.

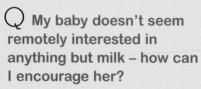

Q **My baby doesn't seem remotely interested in anything but milk – how can I encourage her?**

A At the outset of weaning, it is not crucial that your baby has other fluids, as her usual milk will offer her plenty to keep her hydrated. You can tempt her by offering her a new, brightly coloured cup and allowing her to help herself. You can also give her a cup of water with every meal, so that she becomes used to seeing it there, and considers it a normal part of her meal.

When she has reached eight or nine months and is drinking less milk, you can offer some water. If she won't drink water, you can offer some heavily diluted fruit juice (1 part juice to 10 parts water). Give this after the meal to avoid filling her up, and to help her body absorb the iron from her food. Try also offering her milk in a cup, and gradually diluting it with cooled, boiled water, until there is virtually no milk remaining.

Q **My eight-month-old shows no interest in food; will he be getting enough from breast milk?**

A While some babies are ready for solids by six months or even a little earlier, others take more time. If this is the case, it is important that you see a healthcare professional, as although breast milk is extremely nutritious, it does not contain quite enough iron or vitamin D for babies. It is important that your baby doesn't become deficient in these, and he may require a vitamin supplement.

Furthermore, there is evidence to suggest that babies who are "late" weaners may not take to solid food easily, and resist foods with strong tastes or unusual textures. It's also important to introduce solid food sooner rather than later to give a non-allergic baby a chance to become used to potentially allergenic foods (see page 58).

Make sure you seek advice from a healthcare professional, and continue to offer your baby solid food once or twice a day. If he isn't interested, don't make a fuss. You could try him on some finger foods, which may be more appealing, and which can be "gummed" or sucked until he's ready to take his first bite.

Q I've stopped breastfeeding my six-month-old; will she need formula now?

A Yes, until they reach the age of 12 months, babies need formula milk or breast milk to ensure that they get all of the nutrients they need for optimum growth and development.

"Follow-on" milk, which is higher in iron, may be appropriate at this stage, especially if your baby is a very fussy eater. Discuss this with your doctor or health visitor first.

You can offer solid food, formula, and breast milk together, if that suits you. There is no reason to give up breastfeeding at six months unless both you and your baby are ready. Your baby will need several milk feeds a day until she is a year old.

It's also worth noting that you can use full fat cow's milk, as well as formula, in cooking for your baby or with her cereal at this age.

Q Do I need to use a bottle or can my seven-month-old drink from a cup?

A If your baby can master a cup, and drinks his milk and any other fluids, such as water or baby juice, happily, then there is no reason to introduce a bottle. Many breastfed babies go straight on to a cup from an early age, and manage to get everything they need this way. Your baby may miss the comfort of an evening or morning feed, as drinking from a cup doesn't require the same "sucking", nor a cuddle with mum or dad, so don't rush to lose the bottle or to give up breastfeeding unless you need to. While long-term bottle-feeding can potentially cause damage to teeth, and become a habit, it is also very much a part of babyhood, which is most certainly not over by nine months!

Q Is it safe to mix breast milk with purées?

A You can use breast milk in much the same way as ordinary milk or formula, and blend it into baby purées to add nutrition, and to make them more palatable and "familiar". It is important for babies to have quite runny purées at the outset, as they will "suck" rather than use their lips to remove food from the spoon, and it can take some time to get used to dealing with the food in their mouths before swallowing. Mixing her food with breast milk will ensure it is the right consistency. Remember that, like purées, breast milk has a "shelf life" of 48 hours, and should not be used after this time; add breast milk to purées as and when you use them.

★ offering other drinks

A little heavily diluted juice or water with meals will do no harm, and accustom your baby to drinking from a cup. In fact, a vitamin C-rich juice given at mealtimes will help aid absorption of iron from your baby's food. However, remember that your baby's tummy is very small, and it is easily filled up by drinks, when food is what is really required. Just 30–60ml (1–2 fl oz) of water or juice is fine with meals, preferably after he's eaten. He will likely get all the fluids he needs from milk and purées until weaning is complete.

feeding basics

Every baby is different, both in the way they approach mealtimes and in their individual tastes. There is plenty to consider when you begin weaning, but **try to relax** as you introduce your little one to solid foods, and choose amongst these **tried-and-tested solutions** for the hurdles you might encounter.

Q Where is the best place to feed my baby?

A At first, you may want to feed your baby in her bouncer or even on your lap. As soon as she is able to sit up, it's a good idea to feed her in a highchair in the kitchen, at or by the kitchen table. She'll become used to the concept that people sit down for a meal (hopefully together, as well!), and at a table. Your little one will also understand that when she sits down in her highchair, it's meal time, and not playtime or anything else. She's more likely to concentrate on eating, if this is what she expects. It will also save you a great deal of hassle in the future if she always eats her meals in the same place, as she will understand that dinner in front of the television is not an option.

Finally, it goes without saying that kitchens are much easier than sitting rooms to clean up after your baby has created her usual mess!

Q How often does my baby need to eat solids during the first few weeks?

A Begin by offering solids once a day, around a normal "meal time". Midday is a good time to start, as most little ones won't be too tired, and therefore more willing to try new things. This will also give your baby time to digest the new food, and not struggle with wind during the night. Don't wait until your baby is starving, because he'll want only one thing – his usual milk! Over the next month or so, you can increase the number of solid food meals.

Q When should my baby be eating three meals a day?

A By the age of seven, eight, or nine months your baby should be eating three meals a day, and be ready to enjoy a wide variety of tastes. She should have doubled her birth weight, and a diet of milk may not be enough for her, so it's important to give her red meat, which is a good source of iron and zinc, and oily fish, such as salmon or tuna, which contain essential fatty acids that are important for your baby's brain development. Don't give your baby more than two portions of oily fish a week.

new tastes and textures

With so many delicious, **nutritious foods available**, you can be forgiven for becoming confused about what your baby should and shouldn't be eating. It's a **good idea to start slowly**, and take your time in introducing new foods. Once your baby gets used to the idea that **food can be fun and delicious**, she'll be an instant convert.

Q Should I put off introducing wheat until later?

A Wheat can be introduced to your baby from six months onwards. If there is a history of allergies in your family, you may wish to introduce new foods one at a time and over two or three consecutive days, so that if there is a reaction, you'll know what has caused it.

Q When can I introduce dairy produce?

A By six months, it is perfectly safe to add some cow's milk and dairy products (such as yogurt, cheese, and butter) to food. You can give cow's milk with your baby's cereal, or use it when making a cheese sauce, for example. Again, if there is a history of allergies in your family, follow the advice given above when introducing a new food.

Cow's milk, and other milks, such as soya, rice, and oat milk, can be used in the preparation of your baby's food, but should not be offered in place of his normal milk feeds, which need to be continued until he is at least 12 months old.

When cooking, always use full-fat, rather than low-fat milk, until your baby is at least two years old, as he'll need the calories to fuel his rapid growth.

Q Is it OK to give my six-month-old baby yogurt?

A It's fine to introduce yogurt to your baby from six months. Be careful when choosing yogurts, however, as many contain artificial sweeteners and flavourings that aren't appropriate for babies. Ideally, you'll want to find one without any added sugar, and blended with fresh fruit purée. Many babies prefer fromage frais, because of its creamier consistency; choose one that is free from artificial additives and sweeteners. Otherwise, you are better off adding a little of your own purée to some plain yogurt, and introducing dairy produce this way. Live yogurt is fine for little ones, and will encourage healthy digestion, but all milk products offered to babies should be pasteurized. Make sure you choose whole-milk yogurts, never low-fat, as your baby will need these extra calories.

PREPARATION TIME 2 MINUTES | COOKING TIME ABOUT 15 MINUTES | MAKES 4 BABY PORTIONS

carrot purée

Root vegetables make the **perfect first weaning food** because of their naturally sweet taste and smooth texture when puréed. **Orange-coloured root vegetables** are rich in beta-carotene, which is essential for growth, healthy skin, **good vision, and strong bones.** The recipe will also work for sweet potato, parsnip, or swede.

2 carrots, washed and peeled or scraped, then chopped or sliced

1 Put the carrots in a steamer set over boiling water and cook for 15–20 minutes until really tender (the smaller the pieces, the quicker they'll cook). Alternatively, place the carrots in a saucepan and just cover with boiling water. Bring back to the boil, then reduce the heat and simmer for about 15 minutes or until tender; drain, reserving the cooking liquid.

2 Purée the carrots until very smooth, adding some of the cooking liquid or some of the water in the bottom of the steamer. The amount of liquid you add really depends on your baby – you may need to add more if your baby finds it hard to swallow.

3 Allow to cool, then serve one portion and freeze the remainder in ice cube trays or small pots. If frozen, thaw overnight in the fridge, then reheat in the microwave or a small pan until piping hot. Stir and allow to cool before serving.

PREPARATION TIME 15 MINUTES | COOKING TIME 40 MINUTES | MAKES 5–6 BABY PORTIONS

sweet potato and squash purée

Babies' taste buds tend to be **tuned into sweet flavours,** so naturally sweet fruits and vegetables are popular early foods. **Orange fruits and vegetables** like butternut squash and sweet potato are naturally sweet and they are also high in beta-carotene, which is the **plant form of vitamin A.**

1 small or ½ large butternut squash, peeled, deseeded, and cut into 2.5cm (1in) cubes

1 sweet potato, peeled and cut into 2.5cm (1in) cubes

1 tbsp olive oil

2 tbsp water

A little breast milk or formula

1 Preheat the oven to 200°C (180°C fan), gas 6.

2 Lay a large piece of foil on a baking sheet and spread out the squash and sweet potato on the foil. Drizzle over the olive oil and water. Cover with a second large piece of foil and scrunch the edges of the two foil pieces together to form a parcel. Bake for about 30 minutes or until the vegetables are tender.

3 Cool the vegetables slightly, then transfer to a blender (including any liquid). Blend to a smooth purée. Thin the purée with breast milk or formula to the desired consistency. (If you are going to freeze the purée, add the milk after thawing.)

4 Freeze in individual portions. When needed, thaw for 1–2 hours at room temperature, then microwave or reheat in a small pan until piping hot. Stir and allow to cool before serving.

PREPARATION TIME 10 MINUTES | COOKING TIME 14–15 MINUTES | MAKES 2–3 BABY PORTIONS

beef, squash, and tomato purée

The sweet squash and tomatoes here help to make
the flavour of beef more palatable for fussy babies.
As your baby gets older, the cooked beef can be
mashed into the squash and tomatoes, and served
with small pasta shapes.

2 plum tomatoes

1 tsp olive oil

115g (4oz) extra-lean minced beef

¼ small butternut squash, peeled,
  deseeded, and grated

150ml (5fl oz) vegetable stock, or water

1 Cut a small cross in the top of each tomato. Put
them in a heatproof bowl and cover with freshly
boiled water. Leave to stand for 30 seconds, then
drain and plunge in cold water. Peel off the skins.
Cut the skinned tomatoes into quarters, scoop out
the seeds, and chop the flesh.

2 Heat the olive oil in a large frying pan or wok and
sauté the beef for 2–3 minutes, stirring well, until
browned and crumbly. Add the squash and
chopped tomato, and sauté, stirring, for a further
2 minutes or until the vegetables are softened.
Add the stock and bring to the boil, then reduce
the heat, cover, and simmer for about 10 minutes.

3 Cool slightly before puréeing the contents of the
pan in a blender, adding a little extra boiled water
if the purée is too thick.

4 Freeze in individual portions. When needed, thaw
overnight in the fridge, then reheat until piping
hot. Stir and allow to cool slightly before serving.

PREPARATION 10 MINUTES | COOKING TIME 25 MINUTES | MAKES 600ML (1 PINT)

my favourite chicken purée

This is tasty and **a good introduction to chicken**. Adding a little **sweetness** by combining the **chicken with sweet potato** and dried apricots makes it appealing to babies. I've used chicken thigh as it has a softer, more **moist consistency** than breast, and the **dark meat** of chicken has twice as much **iron and zinc** as the white.

2 chicken thighs

1 tbsp olive oil

50g (scant 2oz) sliced leek

225g (8oz) peeled and chopped
    sweet potato

40g (scant 1½oz) dried apricots, halved

150ml (5fl oz) passata

200ml (7fl oz) chicken stock or water

1 Remove the meat from the chicken thighs and discard the skin and fat. I use about 110g (4oz) chicken thigh meat for this recipe. Cut into chunks.

2 Heat the oil in a pan and sauté the leek for about 4 minutes until softened. Add the chicken and sauté for about 2 minutes until the chunks are white on all sides. Add the sweet potato and sauté for 1 minute. Stir in the dried apricots, passata, and chicken stock. Bring to the boil, then cover and simmer for about 15 minutes. Blend to a purée.

PREPARATION 6 MINUTES, PLUS COOLING | COOKING TIME 55 MINUTES | MAKES 275ML (9½FL OZ)

sweet potato and spinach purée

A good way to introduce **stronger-tasting green vegetables** to your baby is to mix them with root vegetables. Baked sweet potato is particularly good as a base, because **baking this vegetable accentuates its sweetness.** It's worth popping some sweet potatoes into the oven when you are making **a roast for the rest of the family.**

50g (scant 2oz) fresh baby spinach leaves, carefully washed

A generous knob of butter

1 sweet potato (about 250g/9oz), baked and cooled

125ml (4fl oz) milk

1 Put the washed spinach into a pan and cook for about 3 minutes until wilted. Remove the spinach from the pan and press out any excess liquid. Melt the butter in the pan and sauté the spinach for 1 minute.

2 Halve the baked sweet potato and scoop out the flesh, then blend with the sautéed spinach and milk to a purée.

PREPARATION 8 MINUTES | COOKING TIME 15 MINUTES | MAKES 350ML (12FL OZ)

fillet of fish with cheesy vegetable sauce

This makes **a good introduction to fish** for your baby. Plaice is one of the best fish to start with, as it has **a lovely moist, soft texture.** I like to **boost the nutrients** in the cheese sauce by adding steamed carrot and broccoli, which are **rich in vitamins.** If you don't have a microwave, you can poach the fillet of plaice in **a small saucepan of milk** instead.

1 medium carrot, peeled and sliced

40g (scant 1½oz) broccoli florets

1 fillet of plaice (or other white fish fillet), skinned (about 100g/3½oz)

A knob of butter

Sauce

15g (½oz) butter

15g (½oz) plain flour

150ml (5fl oz) milk

40g (scant 1½oz) Cheddar cheese, grated

1 Steam the carrot for 5 minutes, then add the broccoli florets and continue to steam for about 7 minutes until the vegetables are tender. Meanwhile, put the plaice into a suitable microwave dish, dot with butter, and microwave on high for about 1½ minutes.

2 To make the cheese sauce, melt the butter, stir in the flour, and cook over a low heat for 1 minute. Gradually whisk in the milk. Bring to the boil and simmer for a few minutes until thickened and smooth. Remove from the heat and stir in the grated cheese until melted.

3 Blend the vegetables and flaked fish with the cheese sauce to a purée.

★ **Note:** As your baby gets older, you can mash the vegetables and fish with the sauce, rather than making a purée.

PREPARATION TIME 10 MINUTES | COOKING TIME 13–15 MINUTES | MAKES 6 BABY PORTIONS

cauliflower, potato, and cheese purée

This purée is **very filling and thick,** so ideal for hungry babies. If you are using sweet potato **instead of regular white potato,** you can reduce the cooking time of the potato on its own to 3 minutes before you **add the cauliflower.**

1 potato or small sweet potato (175g/6oz), peeled and cut into 1cm (½in) cubes

¼ small cauliflower, cut in little florets

100g (3½oz) Red Leicester or Cheddar cheese, grated

2–4 tbsp breast milk or formula

1 Put the potato cubes in a steamer, spreading them out in one layer. Cover and steam for 5 minutes. Add the cauliflower to the steamer, spreading the florets evenly. Cover again and steam for a further 8–10 minutes until the vegetables are soft.

2 Transfer the vegetables to a blender and add the cheese and 2 tbsp of the breast milk or formula. Blend to a smooth purée, adding extra milk or formula if the purée is too thick.

3 Freeze in individual portions. When needed, thaw overnight in the fridge, then reheat until piping hot. Stir and allow to cool slightly, and check the temperature before serving.

PREPARATION TIME 8 MINUTES | COOKING TIME 6–8 MINUTES | MAKES 3 BABY PORTIONS

sole, sweet potato, and broccoli purée

When **introducing fish** to babies, I like to start with something like sole or plaice as it is very tender and mild. Here I **combine it with sweet vegetables**, which should help to tempt the tastebuds. You can also substitute salmon for the white fish.

½ sweet potato (about 200g/7oz), peeled and cut in small dice

2 broccoli florets (about 40g/1½ oz in total), cut in small pieces

115g (4oz) sole, plaice, or other white fish fillet, skinned and cut into little-finger size strips

4 tbsp milk

20g (¾oz) Gruyère or Emmenthal cheese, grated

1 Spread the sweet potato and broccoli out in a steamer (or use a metal colander set over a pan of simmering water). Cover and steam for 6–8 minutes until really tender.

2 Meanwhile, put the fish into a small saucepan, cover with the milk, and cook for about 2 minutes or until it flakes easily. Remove from the heat and stir in the cheese until melted. Put the vegetables and fish mixture in a blender or baby mouli and purée. Add a little more milk, if necessary.

3 Cool as quickly as possible (put the purée in a glass bowl set in a second bowl of ice and stir for 4–5 minutes), then cover and put into the fridge. Or freeze in individual portions; thaw overnight in the fridge when needed.

4 To serve, heat the purée in a microwave or small saucepan until piping hot, stirring occasionally and adding a little more milk if necessary. Cool to warm and check the temperature before serving.

no-cook baby foods

Each of the purées below takes **no more than a few minutes** to prepare, and makes one serving. You can serve them individually, or mix them. **Good combinations** are avocado and banana; avocado, banana, and yogurt; and **papaya and banana**.

avocado

★ Avocados offer the perfect ratio of good fat (monounsaturated), protein, and carbohydrate, all in one food. Being nutrient-dense, they'll help fuel your baby's rapid growth in the first year. Avocado provides folate and vitamins A and B_3.
  Cut a small, ripe avocado in half, remove the stone, and scoop out the flesh. Mash half with a little of your baby's usual milk until quite smooth.

banana

★ Because bananas are easily portable, they are ideal to take with you when you are out and about and want to feed your baby. Banana provides potassium, magnesium, selenium, and folate.
  Peel half a small, ripe banana and mash with a fork until quite smooth. You may want to mix the mashed banana with a little of your baby's usual milk to thin down the consistency to begin with.

papaya

★ Papaya provides beta-carotene, folate, and vitamins B_3, C, and E, and it contains an enzyme that aids digestion.
  Cut a small, ripe papaya in half, remove the black seeds, and peel. Mash the flesh of half of the papaya until quite smooth. Alternatively, if the papaya flesh is fibrous, purée in a blender.

PREPARATION 10 MINUTES | COOKING TIME 20 MINUTES | MAKES 400ML (14FL OZ) PORTIONS

potato and carrot mash with salmon

It's hard to find jars of baby purée with **oily fish like salmon**, which is the best source of **essential fatty acids** that are **vital for your baby's brain** and visual development. Mashed potato and carrot mixed with **a little milk,** butter, and cheese **makes a good base** for a baby's meal. I prefer to mash potato, because puréeing it in a blender breaks down the **natural starches**, leaving a gloopy texture. If mashed food is too lumpy for your baby, you could try using **a baby food grinder** or potato ricer to prepare this.

300g (10½oz) potatoes, peeled and chopped

100g (3½oz) carrot, peeled and sliced

3½ tbsp milk

Generous knob of butter

40g (scant 1½oz) Cheddar cheese, grated

100g (3½oz) piece of salmon fillet, skinned

1 Put the potatoes and carrot into a saucepan, cover with boiling water, and cook for 20 minutes until the vegetables are tender. Drain and mash together with 3 tbsp milk, the butter, and cheese.

2 While the vegetables are cooking, put the salmon into a suitable microwave dish with the remaining ½ tbsp milk, and microwave on high for 1½ minutes. (If you don't have a microwave, you can steam the fish over the vegetables for 5–6 minutes.) Flake the fish, checking to make sure that there are no bones in it.

3 Mix the fish into the potato and carrot mash, and serve.

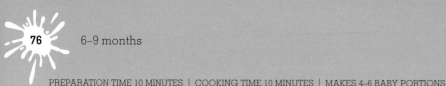
PREPARATION TIME 10 MINUTES | COOKING TIME 10 MINUTES | MAKES 4–6 BABY PORTIONS

chicken and corn chowder

Chicken is a **good first meat for babies** as it is tender and has a mild flavour. Mixing it with sweetcorn in a smooth chowder is **a clever way to introduce chicken** to your baby. Another good combination is chicken with sweet potato and apple.

1 skinless, boneless chicken breast, cut into 2cm (¾in) cubes

200g (7oz) can naturally sweet sweetcorn in water, drained

5 tbsp water

1 potato, peeled and diced

1–2 tbsp breast milk or formula

1 Put the chicken, sweetcorn, and measured water in a small heatproof bowl and set the bowl in a large saucepan. Put the potato in the saucepan alongside the bowl. Pour boiling water over the potato in the pan so the water comes halfway up the sides of the bowl. Bring the water back to the boil, then reduce the heat, cover, and cook for about 10 minutes or until the potato and the chicken are cooked through.

2 Lift the bowl out of the pan. Drain the potatoes and put them in a baby mouli set over a bowl. Add the chicken, sweetcorn, and cooking liquid from the bowl and purée the mixture (puréeing with a mouli will get rid of the skins from the sweetcorn; if you use a blender, you will have to pass the mixture through a sieve after puréeing). Add a little milk, if necessary, to make a soft, smooth consistency. Cool quickly, then chill. Or, freeze in individual portions; thaw overnight in the fridge when needed.

3 To serve, heat in a saucepan or microwave until piping hot. Allow to cool slightly and check the temperature before serving.

PREPARATION TIME 7 MINUTES | COOKING TIME 10–15 MINUTES | MAKES ABOUT 8 BABY PORTIONS

creamy apple and oat purée

"Eating" rather than "cooking" apples will make a sweet purée, with **plenty of nutrients** and healthy fibre. Oats make a great addition to your baby's diet; they are **packed with vitamins**, minerals, and essential fatty acids. Best of all, they help to stabilize your baby's blood sugar levels, **keeping him calm and full of energy**.

3 eating apples, such as Spartan or Pink Lady, peeled, cored, and thinly sliced

2 tbsp water

Pinch of ground cinnamon (optional)

1 tsp agave nectar (optional – to add more sweetness)

Per portion

1 tbsp baby oats

2 tbsp breast milk or formula

1 Put the apples in a saucepan with the water. Bring to the boil, then reduce the heat, cover, and cook very gently for 10–15 minutes until soft.

2 Add the cinnamon, if using, and purée in a blender, or mash. Sweeten with the agave nectar, if using. Cool the purée and keep in the fridge until needed, or freeze in individual portions and thaw as required.

3 To serve, warm one portion (approx 2 tbsp) of the apple purée and stir in the oats and milk. Cool slightly and check the temperature before serving.

balance and variety

As parents **we have a responsibility** to ensure that our little ones get everything they need to grow up **strong and healthy**. That doesn't mean serving boring "health" food, but encouraging a **fresh, delicious and varied diet** that will provide your baby with all the key nutrients she needs.

Q My baby will eat only fruit purées; does this matter?

A In the short-term, it is not a big problem, as your baby will be getting plenty of nutrients from fruit. However, it won't give your baby protein or iron. It does also become an issue if your baby develops a sweet tooth, as he will be reluctant to try anything that is not "sugary", which can make introducing other foods that much more difficult. Fruit is very healthy, but it can cause a surge in blood sugar, followed by a crash, which can leave your baby tired and irritable. Moreover, it can, over time, cause tooth decay.

It's much better to have a mix of both fruit and vegetables. Try different combinations, such as spinach and kiwi, parsnip and apple, or mango with carrots. Try, too, introducing sweeter vegetables, such as sweetcorn, peas, sweet potato, and squash on their own. Their natural sweetness can match the sweetness of fruits.

Q When do I have to start making sure my baby's diet is balanced?

A When you begin weaning, you are offering tastes of a variety of different foods to accustom your baby to the process of eating rather than just drinking her usual milk, and also to encourage her to develop a taste for different flavours and textures. At the outset, she'll probably have only one or two small meals a day, heavily subsidized by her usual milk, which provides the vast majority of the nutrients she requires. When her milk feeds become less frequent, and she is eating more at mealtimes, usually around eight or nine months, it becomes increasingly important that she gets a variety of different nutrients from each of the main food groups: carbohydrates, fats, protein, and vitamins and minerals.

It's not as hard as you may think to ensure that she has a balanced diet. If you aim for plenty of fresh fruit and vegetables, with different foods presented every day or so, plus some good-quality protein, such as red meat, poultry, pulses, and fish, some healthy carbs (wholegrains are your best choice here), and some dairy produce and eggs, too, your baby will be getting exactly what she needs.

Q We want to raise our baby as a vegetarian; is there anything extra he needs at this age?

A To begin with, a vegetarian baby's diet is the same as for other babies – a variety of fresh fruits and vegetables. Introduce your baby to the huge variety of delicious vegetables available, and encourage him to try as many as he can, so that your options are not limited as he gets older.

The iron a baby inherits from his mother runs out at around six months, so from six or seven months, you should include iron-rich foods, such as pulses (lentils and chickpeas), leafy green vegetables, eggs, and dried apricots, in your baby's diet. Wholegrain cereals are also a good source, but do not give your baby too many, as his tummy is only small. It's important to include foods like cheese and well-cooked eggs too. These are good sources of protein and vitamin B12, which your baby needs for growth and development.

Being vegan, however, does mean cutting out two further main food groups: dairy and egg. These must be carefully replaced, so it may be useful to see a trained dietitian. Also, if you give your baby at least 600ml (20fl oz) of fortified infant soya formula daily, until he is two, he shouldn't need supplements.

Q How can I introduce pulses into my baby's diet?

A Lentils, peas, chickpeas, and beans, such as butter beans and cannellini beans, are all good first foods, and will offer plenty of protein and iron, as well as fibre and B vitamins, so are great for vegetarian babies. Cook them thoroughly, and purée them with vegetables to make them more tasty, and easier to swallow and digest (see my red lentils purée recipe on page 105).

Your baby doesn't need many of any type of pulse at this stage and age – a serving would constitute no more than four or five individual peas or beans, or a spoonful of lentils. So even adding a teaspoon of cooked pulses to your baby's normal purée, and whizzing them together, will provide some added nutrition, and a different, unique texture. Many babies love hummus – look out for brands with no added salt or make your own. Serve on toast fingers, pitta bread, or with carrot, cucumber, and other veggies.

⭐ did you know ...

that carrots and other brightly coloured fruits and vegetables contain highly nutritious nutrients known as carotenoids, which your baby's body converts to vitamin A? This vitamin is crucial for health and development, and encourages healthy vision, immune system function, and strong, healthy bones. If possible, steam rather than boil carrots, as this allows the beta-carotene to be more bio-available and readily used by the body.

feeding problems

Some babies find **the transition to solid foods** easy, while others can be more resistant. Try to stick to a daily routine, even if you are out and about, or on holiday. It's not always easy, but **with a little ingenuity** and a good thermos flask, you'll soon overcome any problems.

Q **My baby refuses the same foods over and over again; how can I tempt him to eat more foods?**

A Perseverance is the order of the day. Simply continue to offer the "new" foods over and over again, until they become familiar to your baby (see opposite page). You can try them in different combinations – for example, mixing spinach with some apple purée or even a little Parmesan cheese and his normal baby milk, adding apricots to sweet potato, and pear to peas. Once you find one or two things you know he likes, you can use these as a base for creating different blends.

Remember too that many babies have quite sophisticated tastes. Baby food doesn't have to be bland, and your little one may enjoy trying exciting tastes that you may not have considered, such as garlic or a touch of mild curry paste in the cooking.

Q **Can you recommend some combinations of vegetables to appeal to my faddy baby?**

A Some of the best vegetables are those that are sweet. Fortunately, most of these all contain good levels of vitamins and minerals, and, in particular, antioxidants, which will ensure that your child grows and develops, and maintains good health.

Try sweet potato, squash, sweetcorn, peas, edamame beans, butter beans, carrots, potato, courgettes, parsnips, and even avocado. Any combination of these will work. See page 66 for my delicious Sweet potato and squash purée recipe. If your little one has already expressed a preference for fruit purées, you can blend a little into your vegetable blends for added sweetness and flavour. Don't be afraid to experiment. I like root vegetables together, such as parsnip, carrot and potato, or butternut squash with very ripe pear. Sweet vegetables, such as carrot, puréed with fish or chicken is also a favourite with many babies.

Again, persevere, if you can tempt your baby to eat vegetables early on, she'll be much more likely to continue.

Q My baby likes only one type of food, and refuses everything else; any advice?

A Babies easily become accustomed to the familiar, and if he's found a particular food he likes, such as apple purée or carrot purée, and had it offered on a number of occasions, he may be reluctant to try anything else – and he may also hold out until he gets what he wants. Don't underestimate the determination of even very young babies.

The best thing to do is to continue offering new foods; over time (and this can take up to 15 or 20 attempts in some cases), the new food will become familiar, and he'll accept it. Try mixing his favourite food with other fruits and vegetables, adding small quantities at the outset, and then gradually more until he is getting a variety of different tastes.

If your baby is very young, he may find the process of weaning a little upsetting – in fact, some babies are more sensitive to change than others – so it may help to mix new foods such as green vegetables with popular "first tastes", for example sweet-tasting root vegetables, to make them more comforting. Remember to take weaning slowly, and follow your baby's own pace. Some little ones take to it quickly and move on to a variety of different foods with no fuss; others need a little more time to adjust to the change.

It can also help to eat the same meals as your little one. If he sees you, and perhaps the rest of the family, clearly enjoying a variety of different foods, he may want to follow suit. Make a "mmmm" sound when you offer them; it may sound simple, but if he is convinced that what he is trying is delicious, he'll respond much more positively. Whatever you do, don't panic or make a fuss. Simply remove the food and try again later.

Q Is there any way to bring homemade purées on holiday?

A If you don't have far to travel, you can pack several trays of frozen purée along with some cool packs and other frozen items, to ensure they remain at the lowest possible temperature while in transit. This may not be feasible, though, and perhaps more trouble than it's worth.

There are, however, plenty of ways to make fresh purées that don't even require cooking, and if you have a kitchen to hand, you can easily whip up the odd fresh purée as and when you need to! Exotic fruits like mango, peach, or papaya make perfect baby food and they don't even need any cooking (see page 118). See the following pages, too, for some great recipe suggestions, requiring little more than a knife, fork, and bowl. For older babies, a wedge of peeled mango or melon makes good finger food.

★ transporting purées

For days out, you could invest in a small wide-necked thermos flask that will keep your baby's purée warm. The cover will serve as your baby's food bowl. If there is a fridge at your destination, a good cool bag with an ice pack should keep your baby's purée fresh until you reach your destination. The purées will then last a couple of days in the fridge.

PREPARATION TIME 3–5 MINUTES | EACH RECIPE MAKES 1 BABY PORTION

quick fruit purées

It can be difficult to provide healthy, homemade food for your baby on holiday. These **simple, no-cook purées** can be prepared in just a few minutes with basic cutlery and your baby's feeding bowl.

avocado and banana or pear
★ Scoop out the flesh from ¼–½ small, ripe avocado and mash with a fork. Mash ¼–½ small, ripe banana or pear (peeled and cored). Beat into the avocado until smooth.

banana and mango
★ Peel ¼–½ small, ripe mango, remove the flesh, and mash with a fork. Mash ¼–½ small, ripe banana into the mango and beat well until smooth.

banana and peach
★ Pull the skin off 1 small, ripe peach with the help of a knife. Remove the stone and mash the flesh. Mash ¼–½ small, ripe banana into the peach and beat well until smooth.

cantaloupe melon
★ Scoop out the seeds from 1 small slice of ripe melon, then cut off the skin. Cut the flesh into small pieces. Mash with a fork, then beat until smooth.

pear (or pear with peach)
★ Peel and core 1 small, ripe pear (or ½ small pear and ½ small, ripe peach). Cut the flesh into small pieces and mash with a fork, then beat until smooth.

PREPARATION TIME 10 MINUTES | COOKING TIME 10 MINUTES | MAKES 4–6 BABY PORTIONS

peach, apple, and pear purée

Ripe, seasonal fruits can make a plain apple purée a little more interesting. I like to use peaches or nectarines, **but apricots or plums are also good.** If the fruit is not very sweet, you can add a teaspoon of agave nectar, which is available from health food shops and some supermarkets.

2 ripe peaches

1 eating apple, such as Spartan or Pink Lady, peeled, cored, and diced

1 ripe pear, peeled, cored, and diced

2 tbsp water

1 Cut a small cross in the top and bottom of each peach and put them in a heatproof bowl. Cover with freshly boiled water and leave to stand for 30 seconds, then drain and plunge in cold water. Peel off the skins. Cut the peaches into quarters, remove the stones, and dice the flesh.

2 Put the diced peaches, apple, and pear in a saucepan with the water. Bring to the boil, then cover, reduce the heat to low, and cook gently for about 10 minutes or until the juices have run from the peaches and the fruits are all soft.

3 Cool slightly, then tip into a blender and purée until smooth. Serve warm, or cool quickly and chill in the fridge before serving. The purée can be frozen in individual portions; thaw for 1–2 hours at room temperature when needed.

PREPARATION 8 MINUTES | COOKING TIME 8 MINUTES | MAKES 400ML (14FL OZ) FRUIT PURÉE

porridge with apple, pear, and apricot

This makes a **nutritious breakfast** and is suitable from six months. Pack up portions of the fruit purée and freeze. Then you can thaw them overnight, ready to mix with your **baby's porridge** in the morning. **As your baby gets older**, you can simply stir in rather than purée.

1 apple, peeled, cored, and chopped

1 ripe pear, peeled, cored, and chopped

4 ready-to-eat dried apricots, chopped

To serve (per portion)

6 tbsp milk

1 heaped tbsp porridge oats

1 Put the fruit into a saucepan with 4 tbsp water. Cover and cook for about 6 minutes until tender. Allow to cool, then blend to a purée.

2 To make the porridge, combine the milk and oats in another small saucepan. Bring to the boil, then simmer, stirring occasionally, for about 3 minutes. Combine the fruit and the porridge, and blend to a purée.

PREPARATION TIME 10 MINUTES | COOKING TIME 9–11 MINUTES | MAKES 5 BABY PORTIONS

superfoods purée

Superfoods have been identified as **those rich in vitamins, minerals, and antioxidants**. This purée contains turkey, spinach, and sweet potatoes, which all make the grade. You can also use **minced chicken thigh** instead of the turkey.

1 sweet potato, peeled and cut into 1cm (½in) cubes

2 tsp olive oil

1 small shallot, or small piece of onion, finely chopped

115g (4oz) minced turkey

2 handfuls of baby spinach leaves, washed but not dried

1 Put the sweet potato in a steamer and steam for about 6 minutes or until tender. Remove from the steamer and reserve the steaming water.

2 While the sweet potato is cooking, heat the oil in a large frying pan or wok, add the chopped shallot and turkey, and stir-fry for 2–3 minutes until the turkey is browned and crumbly. Add the spinach and sauté for 2–3 minutes until wilted.

3 Add the cooked sweet potato and 4 tbsp of the steaming water. Cover and simmer gently for 5 minutes.

4 Put the contents of the pan in a blender and blend to a purée. Thin with a little of the steaming water, if necessary. Cool quickly, then chill. Freeze in individual portions, then thaw overnight in the fridge when needed.

5 To serve, heat in a saucepan or microwave until piping hot. Allow to cool slightly and check the temperature before serving.

chapter 3

9–12 months:
exploring new tastes

9–12 months:
what you can expect

Your baby will now be showing signs of becoming **an accomplished and self-sufficient eater**. She'll be curious about food, and may be willing to **explore new tastes and textures,** particularly when the rest of the family are doing the same!

Q Can I let my baby feed herself now?

A It's a good idea to encourage your baby to feed herself, and this will develop a wide range of the skills that will eventually be involved in self-feeding, and other manual activities. However, most little ones are unable to feed themselves properly until they are at least two or three years old, and until that time, they will rely on mum, dad, or carer to ensure that the right amount of food is fed into their mouths.

Q Should I allow my baby to use his hands to eat and play with his food?

A This is an important part of the developmental process of learning to eat and to become accustomed to solid foods, and it should be encouraged. The mess may drive you crazy, but your baby should be allowed to touch and feel his food, and to guide it in the direction of his mouth without admonishment. He'll discover the different textures – the way they feel and taste – and will be interested in uncovering new wonders as he gets a little older.

Q How can I encourage my baby to be a little neater while eating?

A Neatness and babies don't really go together when it comes to food. Try to be patient, and allow her to experiment and explore what's on offer. You can discourage her from throwing food or rubbing her mucky hands on the walls or her high chair by taking away her bowl each time she does this, expressing your disapproval, and making her realize that it is unacceptable. However, normal messiness, which can involve a good proportion of the room as well as her face, hands, bib, and clothing, is acceptable and she will soon outgrow the stage.

Q My baby takes only a little solid food; does it matter yet?

A Solids form an important part of your baby's diet after six months of age. If your baby does not eat a lot of solids, it's worth discussing with your doctor or health visitor to ensure that he is getting all the nutrients he needs for normal growth and development.

Q How can I encourage my baby to try new tastes?

A Encourage your baby to experiment! Allow her to try some tastes from your plate, and give her bits when you are preparing food – to lick, suck, "gum", eat, or smell. The more familiar she becomes with various foods, the more adventurous she will be when it comes to eating a wider variety. Once she has passed the first foods stage, offer something new at every meal – consider each food type "new" until she's decided to accept it.

★ talking the talk

Use the same words over and over while mimicking the action you want your baby to adopt – "eat with your spoon" for example. Within a couple of weeks your baby will understand that the words you say mean something specific and be able to carry out the action you are describing.

breast milk and more

Although your baby's diet will be expanding dramatically over the coming months, his usual milk will remain **a large part of his diet until he approaches his first birthday.** It's reassuring to know that if your little one is a slow weaner or a faddy eater, the nutrients in breast milk or formula will help him to **grow and develop.**

Q How much milk should my baby be having at this age?

A Until your baby is at least 12 months old, she will need, at the very minimum, 600ml (1 pint) of formula milk or breast milk every single day. Some babies might need more, particularly if they are heavier and growing quickly. During growth spurts, even more milk may be required, so do try to meet your baby's demands, thereby making sure her body's nutritional needs are met. She'll let you know if she's not getting enough.

Q How much water do babies need?

A If your baby is being breastfed, he will need no extra fluid at all. However, if he's thirsty, by all means offer a little cooled, previously boiled water or some very diluted fruit juice. Bottle-fed babies often need more fluids, but because their food at this stage tends to be quite watery, and is typically based on fruits and vegetables, which have a high liquid content, they really don't need much. You could offer 30–60ml (1–2fl oz) of water two or three times a day, and if he drinks it all, offer more. Try to assess what your baby needs, and then act accordingly. Be sure that your baby is getting enough milk – this provides him with a great deal of liquid (see left).

★ did you know ...

that smoothies are a fantastic way to offer fruit (and vegetables) to babies, as they are effectively purées in a more liquid form? It's important to consider the number of fruits involved – the equivalent of a shot glass is plenty – if you are to avoid upsetting your little one's digestion. Berries, ripe bananas, mangos, grapes, papaya, and pears all provide the basis for a great smoothie. Throw in some cucumber, bell pepper, or carrot juice to increase the nutrient factor.

Q Do I need to stop breastfeeding now that my baby has teeth?

A There is no need to stop breastfeeding as long as both you and your baby enjoy it. While the introduction of teeth can cause a little discomfort in the early days, if your baby tries to use your breast as a teething ring, or accidentally or playfully bites you, if she is latched on correctly, teeth will make no difference to the process. In fact, you can be sure that your nutritious milk is helping to produce even healthier teeth! The World Health Organization suggests that breastfeeding should be continued for two years. This may seem a long time at this point, but it's something to aspire to, if you can manage it.

Q My baby seems to think it's funny to bite me; what can I do?

A Babies love to experiment with their new skills and tools, and may realize that they get an instant reaction by using their teeth to best effect. Making mummy shriek may seem very amusing, but it's important that you lay down the law early on, or you will have very sore breasts, and your baby may find that his nursing days are over. Say "no" very firmly when your baby bites you, and remove him from the breast. He may become distressed, and want to return. That's fine, but if he does it again, remove him and leave it for longer. He'll soon learn that he won't get his usual feed if he nips. Try to wait until your baby is hungry before offering him a feed. A hungry baby will not usually bother with games. If he's in a playful mood and just wants a little comfort, amuse him with games, stories, and songs instead, or offer a cuddle. Babies are more likely to bite if they aren't fully engaged in feeding, so some pre-emptive action might save you from a little pain.

Q Do I need to breastfeed for longer if my baby seems to suffer from reactions to food?

A There is quite a lot of evidence to suggest that long-term breastfeeding does offer some protection from allergies. It is, however, very important that your diet does not contain any of the foods that are considered to be problematic, and you will be able to establish exactly what these foods are only with the help of an allergy specialist. In the short and long term, however, you will be offering your baby your own antibodies through breastfeeding, which will help to prop up her immature immune system. So, offering your baby breast milk for longer will ensure that she gets the nutrients, calories, and antibodies she needs to grow and develop properly, and minimize the risk of allergies.

Q Can a drink of juice or another snack take the place of a feed when I am weaning?

A No, babies do need their regular milk to provide them with the right calories and nutrients for growth and development. You may find that your baby is hungry or thirsty between feeds and meals, at which point it is fine to offer an extra drink or a healthy snack. If it's close to a mealtime, try to stave her off, so that she will eat enough healthy food to keep her going.

fun with finger foods

Finger foods are a wonderful way to introduce your baby to various **tastes and textures**, and will help to encourage independent eating. Your baby will enjoy **the process of feeding himself** as well as **the new variety of foods** that you offer. The more you encourage this process, the easier the transition will be.

Q How do we progress from purées to lumps?

A The simple answer is a little at a time. All babies develop at different paces, but by now your baby should be a confident purée eater, and will probably have mastered some finger foods. Not all babies find the transition easy, and some actively avoid lumps for as long as they can. Try to stay calm and work at your baby's pace.

You can begin by mashing rather than puréeing some of her favourite foods, as these will be familiar to her, and she'll find the process less daunting. You can also try adding a few of her usual finger foods to her purées – some toast fingers alongside her puréed vegetables, or some mini pasta shapes stirred into her broccoli with cheese. Let her get used to every stage before rushing her on. You are much better off letting her explore mashed foods for a few weeks before moving to finely chopped.

Q How can I tell if my baby is ready for finger foods?

A There are two schools of thought about this one. Some people believe that finger foods should be offered first, and in many cases instead of purées. Others believe that purées should be offered first, and when babies are developmentally ready to pick up, bite, chew, and swallow finger foods, they can be offered – somewhere after nine months. Personally, I think that there is no reason why the two approaches can't be combined. If your baby is a confident eater, offering a variety of finger foods alongside purées is a good way to accustom him to different textures and tastes, and also encourages him to learn the basics of self-feeding. Babies naturally begin to pick things up and explore them, inevitably putting them into their mouths, at around five or six months. From this point on, offering food instead of a toy can provide a nice introduction to the exciting world of food! Be careful what you choose: your baby should be able to gnaw the food without choking or gagging, and be able to derive enough taste by working on it with his gums or budding teeth. Always supervise your baby when he is eating finger food, no matter what his age.

Q How do I introduce finger foods?

A I would suggest offering finger foods at every mealtime, alongside your baby's normal purées, but only after you have established several different fruits, vegetables, and other foods that have been successfully introduced, without any adverse reactions or effects. I've also found that it's useful to have a bowl with several different compartments for holding a range of different finger foods.

Offering finger foods does help to teach your baby to feed herself, and to increase her food repertoire a little. If she picks something up and tastes it, she may not like it to begin with or for the first few times she tries it, but eventually she may consider it to be familiar enough to eat.

Q Which are the best first finger foods for my baby?

A Select easy-to-manage foods that your baby should be able to "gum" to a suitable consistency for swallowing. There is plenty of choice: go for pieces of fruit (melon, apple, pear, banana, kiwi fruit), lightly steamed vegetables (carrot, green beans, broccoli, new potatoes), little sandwiches with healthy fillings, rice cakes, small chunks of cheese, cucumber sticks, hard-boiled egg, oven-baked potato, healthy wholemeal breakfast cereals, berries, dried fruits, well-cooked pasta shapes, toast fingers, and the like. Choose brightly coloured fruits for their enhanced nutritional value, and wholemeal goodies over those that have been refined. You can even offer foods, such as my delicious fish goujons (see page 136) or chicken meatballs without the sauce (see pages 182–83), which your baby can taste, suck, and gnaw at.

Q My baby won't try any of the finger foods I've offered! How can I encourage him to eat them?

A Don't panic! Some babies are slow starters, and may well need a little encouragement to pick up food, move it round their mouths, and then swallow. It's a lot to take on board, and can take a little time. Why not try cutting his foods into fun shapes, such as stars, or use a biscuit cutter to create a cat or a moon? You can also try arranging the finger foods as a picture – a smiley face, perhaps. Some babies find it easier to hold larger pieces, such as a whole carrot. Brightly coloured foods always appeal more to little ones; try topping toast fingers with Red Leicester cheese, and grilling, or offer a selection of fresh fruit chunks with his dry cereal.

★ tempting family food

One good way to encourage your little one to eat foods that are a little chunkier is to offer her food that the whole family is eating, perhaps offering mashed potatoes, a little minestrone soup, or rice mixed with small chunks of chicken. She'll feel very grown up eating what everyone else has on their plates, and may not notice the change in texture.

PREPARATION 4–5 MINUTES | MAKES 1 PORTION

my first muesli

Baby **porridge oats** are nice and fine so make a **good base** on which to add extra – and new – **textures.**

2 tbsp baby porridge oats

2 tbsp milk (or breast milk or formula)

1 tbsp strawberry or vanilla yogurt

½ small banana, mashed or diced

1 Mix the oats, milk, and yogurt together, then stir in the banana. Add a little extra milk if your baby likes a runnier consistency.

PREPARATION 5 MINUTES | COOKING TIME 4-5 MINUTES | MAKES 1 PORTION

french toast fingers

Cinnamon raisin bread makes a nice alternative to ordinary bread for French toast (also called *pain perdu* or **eggy bread**) – it reminds me of **bread and butter pudding**. If you don't have any handy then you can simply add a good pinch of cinnamon to the egg mixture and serve the **French toast** with a few raisins. **Flattening the bread** makes it easier for small mouths to chew.

1 small slice cinnamon raisin bread

1 egg yolk

1 tsp cream (or milk)

1–2 drops of pure vanilla extract

Pinch of caster sugar

15g (½oz) butter

1 Flatten the bread by rolling it out with a rolling pin until it is about half of its original thickness. Beat the egg yolk, cream, vanilla extract, and sugar together in a flat dish.

2 Melt the butter in a frying pan over a medium heat. When the butter is foaming, dip the bread into the egg mixture, then fry in the hot butter for about 2 minutes on each side until golden. Allow to cool until warm, then serve cut into fingers.

★ **Note:** To make two portions, use a whole egg and double everything else.

PREPARATION TIME 10 MINUTES | COOKING TIME 45 MINUTES, PLUS PASTA COOKING | MAKES 6 BABY PORTIONS

my first tomato sauce, with pasta stars

Sweet vegetables blended with tomato make a nice early pasta sauce for babies, helping them to **get used to the new texture** of pasta. Small stars or alphabetti are ideal first pastas as they are **easy to swallow.** You could also use couscous.

1 tbsp olive oil

½ small red onion, chopped

¼ small butternut squash, peeled, deseeded, and grated

1 carrot, peeled and grated

400g (14oz) can chopped tomatoes

120ml (4fl oz) vegetable stock or water

1 tbsp tomato purée

1 tsp soft light brown sugar

Pepper

Per portion

1–2 tbsp pasta stars or other small shapes (according to appetite)

1 tbsp grated Cheddar cheese (optional)

1 Heat the oil in a large frying pan or wok and gently sauté the onion, squash, and carrot, stirring, for 3–4 minutes until softened but not browned. Add the tomatoes, stock, tomato purée, and sugar. Bring to the boil, then reduce the heat, part-cover, and simmer for about 40 minutes or until thickened. Season to taste with a little pepper.

2 Cool slightly, then blend to a purée. The sauce can be frozen in individual portions; when needed, thaw for 1 hour at room temperature, or in a microwave for 30–60 seconds.

3 To serve, cook the pasta according to packet instructions. Drain and return to the pan, then stir in the pasta sauce and cheese, if using. Stir until the cheese melts and the sauce is piping hot. Cool slightly before serving.

PREPARATION TIME 5 MINUTES | COOKING TIME 20 MINUTES | MAKES 2 BABY PORTIONS

oven-baked sweet potato wedges

These sweet potato wedges are **a tasty and healthy alternative** to chips. **I have left the skin on** the potato as it contains a lot of extra vitamins and fibre. To vary, sprinkle on some Parmesan; or, for babies over a year, **make the wedges spicy**. They are good served with a soured cream and chive dip.

1 small sweet potato, scrubbed

2 tsp olive oil

1 tbsp finely grated Parmesan (optional)

For older babies (optional)

Salt and pepper and a good pinch
   of paprika

Or a good pinch of fajita seasoning

1 Preheat the oven to 200°C (180°C fan), gas 6.

2 Cut the potato lengthways into about eight wedges. Put the oil in a bowl, add the wedges, and toss to coat. For babies over one, season with a little salt and pepper and the paprika, or the fajita seasoning, if using.

3 Lay the wedges on a baking sheet lined with baking parchment, spacing them out. Bake for about 10 minutes, then turn them over and bake for another 10 minutes or until tender. If you are not using the spices, you can sprinkle the wedges with the Parmesan, then bake for 1 minute.

4 Cool slightly before serving. Once cooled completely, the wedges can be stored in the fridge for 1 day. Reheat in a dry non-stick frying pan for 2–3 minutes, turning once.

PREPARATION TIME 10 MINUTES | COOKING TIME 30 MINUTES | MAKES 2–3 BABY PORTIONS

chicken and apricot curry

While a very hot curry may **not hit the spot for babies,** a mild and creamy one is often popular. This recipe is a good way to tempt your baby to try **more exciting foods from an early age.**

1 tsp sunflower oil

1 small shallot, finely chopped

2 tsp korma or mild curry paste
(or to taste)

200ml (7fl oz) coconut milk
(or ½ x 400g/14 oz can)

4 ready-to-eat dried apricots, chopped

1 skinless, boneless chicken breast,
or 2 skinless, boneless chicken thighs,
cut into small cubes

To serve

Cooked white rice or couscous

1 Heat the oil in a saucepan and sauté the shallot very gently for 1 minute to soften. Add the curry paste and cook gently for 30 seconds, stirring. Stir in the coconut milk and apricots. Bring to the boil, then reduce the heat and simmer for about 5 minutes or until the apricots start to soften.

2 Add the chicken and stir well, then part-cover and simmer, stirring occasionally, for about 20 minutes or until the chicken and apricots are both tender and the sauce is reduced and thick.

3 The curry is quite soft and so is "gummable", but you can mash or purée it to your baby's preferred consistency. Allow to cool slightly and serve warm, with rice or couscous.

4 The curry can be frozen in individual portions; thaw overnight in the fridge when needed. Add 1 tsp water per portion and heat until piping hot in the microwave or in a saucepan. Cool slightly and check the temperature before serving.

PREPARATION TIME 5 MINUTES | COOKING TIME 25 MINUTES | MAKES 4–5 BABY PORTIONS

red lentils with carrot and tomato

Carrots are a **good source of antioxidants**, and tomatoes contain lycopene, which is also a strong antioxidant. Quick-cooking red lentils are a good **source of folate, fibre, and iron**, so all together these ingredients make a power-packed orange purée.

1 tbsp sunflower oil

2 large tomatoes, skinned (see page 67), deseeded, and chopped

2 carrots, grated

¼ tsp ground coriander

¼ tsp ground cumin (optional)

115g (4oz) red lentils

200ml (7fl oz) coconut milk (or ½ x 400g/14 oz can)

300ml (10fl oz) vegetable stock, or water

1 Heat the oil in a saucepan and sauté the tomatoes and carrots gently, stirring, for about 5 minutes or until softened. Stir in the coriander and cumin, if using, and cook for 30 seconds. Add the lentils, coconut milk, and stock and stir well to mix.

2 Bring to the boil, then reduce the heat, cover, and simmer very gently, stirring occasionally, for about 20 minutes or until the lentils are soft. Add 1–2 tbsp water if the mix gets too dry during cooking.

3 Cool slightly, then transfer to a blender and blend to a purée. Alternatively, mash to the desired consistency. Serve warm.

4 The purée can be frozen in individual portions; when needed, thaw for about 1 hour at room temperature, or about 1 minute in the microwave on Medium Low, then reheat until piping hot. Stir and allow to cool slightly before serving.

PREPARATION TIME 5 MINUTES | COOKING TIME 10 MINUTES | MAKES ABOUT 6 BABY PORTIONS

salmon, carrot, and peas with cheddar

Salmon is a **very nutritious fish,** but it has quite a strong flavour that your baby might not like at a first try. **Mixing it with potato and carrot will** make it seem more familiar.

150ml (5fl oz) vegetable stock, or water

½ potato, peeled and cut in small dice

1 carrot, peeled and cut in small dice

115g (4oz) skinless, boneless salmon fillet, cut into 1cm (½in) cubes

2 tbsp frozen peas (preferably petit pois)

30g (1oz) mild Cheddar cheese, grated

1–2 tbsp breast milk or formula

1 Put the stock in a saucepan with the potato and carrot. Bring to the boil, then reduce the heat, cover, and simmer gently for about 6 minutes or until the potato and carrot are just tender.

2 Add the salmon and peas, cover again, and simmer for 3–4 minutes until the fish flakes easily and all the vegetables are tender.

3 Transfer the contents of the saucepan to a bowl and add the grated cheese. Mash to the desired consistency, adding a little breast milk or formula, if necessary. The mixture can also be blended to a purée if your baby prefers a smooth texture.

4 Cool as quickly as possible, then cover and chill. This can be frozen in individual portions; thaw overnight in the fridge, then reheat until piping hot. Stir and allow to cool slightly before serving.

PREPARATION 2 MINUTES | COOKING TIME 20-25 MINUTES | MAKES 4 PORTIONS

perfectly poached chicken

I usually have **cooked chicken** in my fridge as it is a **handy standby** for snacks and meals. Poaching is a nice way of **cooking chicken breast** as it helps to keep it moist.

150g (5½oz) skinless, boneless chicken breast

600–750ml (1–1¼ pints) chicken stock

1 Put the chicken breast in a saucepan and add enough stock to cover. Put the pan over a medium heat and bring to the boil, then reduce the heat to a very low simmer and poach the chicken for 15 minutes. Turn the breast over and cook for a further 5–10 minutes until the chicken is thoroughly cooked. To check, make a small cut in the side of the chicken breast and peek in to make sure the meat has turned white all the way through.

2 Transfer the chicken to a plate (reserve the stock to use in soups and sauces) and cool for 5 minutes, then shred the chicken into small pieces using two forks, going along the grain of the chicken. Cool completely and refrigerate as quickly as possible.

PREPARATION 5 MINUTES | COOKING TIME 10 MINUTES | MAKES 2 PORTIONS

chicken with easy white sauce

This simple dish is **hearty and filling**. It's also a good way of enhancing the **poached chicken** recipe on the opposite page.

75g (2½oz) shredded chicken with 150ml (5fl oz) of its stock (see opposite)

15g (½oz) butter

1 small shallot, diced

15g (½oz) plain flour

3 tbsp double cream

2 tbsp frozen peas

1 Melt the butter in a pan, add the shallot, and sauté for 5 minutes until softened. Stir in the flour and cook for 1 minute. Remove from the heat. Stir in the stock a little at a time to make a smooth sauce. Return to the heat and slowly bring to a simmer, stirring until thickened.

2 Add the cream, peas, and shredded chicken. Simmer for 2 minutes until everything is hot. (Reheat leftovers in the microwave for about 2 minutes, stirring halfway, until piping hot.) Allow to cool to warm before serving.

PREPARATION 25 MINUTES, PLUS OPTIONAL OVERNIGHT CHILLING | COOKING TIME 4 MINUTES | MAKES 24–26

finger-size salmon fishcakes

These fishcakes are crumbed so they **aren't too squishy** to survive **being picked up,** but for older children (who eat with forks), you could make tablespoon-sized cakes and just **dust them in flour** before frying. **The ketchup in this recipe** gives a subtle tang – add more if you like.

1 medium potato (about 250g/9oz)

150g (5½oz) store-bought poached salmon, skin removed

1 large or 2 small spring onions, finely chopped

1 tbsp mayonnaise

3–4 tsp tomato ketchup (to taste)

2 tbsp plain flour

1 egg, beaten

4 tbsp dried breadcrumbs

3 tbsp freshly grated Parmesan cheese

5–6 tbsp sunflower oil, for frying

1 Microwave the potato for 7–9 minutes until soft. Leave to stand for 10 minutes or until cool enough to handle, then peel off the skin with a sharp knife.

2 Put the potato in a bowl and mash well. Flake the salmon and stir into the potato together with the spring onions, mayonnaise, and ketchup. Mix well – you don't want any large pieces of salmon. Roll teaspoonfuls of the mixture into small balls.

3 Put the flour on a plate; put the egg in a bowl; mix the breadcrumbs and Parmesan together on another plate. Dust the balls with flour, then dip in egg and coat in breadcrumbs. For best results, cover and chill overnight.

4 Heat the oil in a frying pan and cook the fishcakes for about 4 minutes, turning occasionally, until golden brown on all sides. Drain on kitchen paper and allow to cool to warm before serving.

★ **Note:** To freeze, open freeze, then store in a freezer bag; cook from frozen, adding 1 minute to the cooking time.

PREPARATION 5 MINUTES | COOKING TIME 3-4 MINUTES | MAKES 1 PORTION

cheesy scrambled eggs

Well-cooked scrambled eggs are fine for your baby from around six months – egg allergies are less common than most people think. It's a pity not to give children eggs as they are **so quick and easy** to prepare and **so nutritious.** If you prefer, leave out the spring onion, and try using other types of cheese. **Double the quantities for hungry children.**

1 egg

1½ tsp milk

Knob of butter

1 small spring onion, sliced

1 small tomato, skinned, deseeded, and chopped

Small handful of grated Cheddar cheese

1 Beat the egg with the milk. Melt the butter in a medium saucepan and, when foaming, add the spring onion and cook for 30 seconds.

2 Add the eggs with the chopped tomato and cook gently, stirring, until scrambled. Remove from the heat, sprinkle over the cheese, and stir in until slightly melted.

PREPARATION 5 MINUTES | COOKING TIME 6–8 MINUTES | MAKES 1 PORTION

creamy courgette rice

I tend to make this as a quick and **easy side dish** for griddled chicken. You could double the quantities and add 2 tsp **freshly grated Parmesan** if you want to make it a meal in itself.

¼ medium courgette (50g/scant 2oz)

Small knob of butter

3 tbsp cooked rice

2 tbsp milk

1 Grate the courgette on the fine side of a box grater. Melt the butter in a saucepan, add the courgette, and cook gently for 5–6 minutes until the courgette is soft.

2 Stir in the rice and milk. Bring up to a simmer and cook for 1–2 minutes until the rice is hot and the milk is almost completely absorbed. Cool slightly before serving.

PREPARATION 5–8 MINUTES | MAKES 1–2 PORTIONS

finger food sandwiches

The **trick to good sandwiches** is not to have too much bread or too much filling. I like to flatten the bread by **rolling with a rolling pin** so that the sandwich is easier for small children to eat. For toddlers it is best to **cut the sandwich into bite-size pieces**, but as your child gets older it is fun to cut the sandwiches into fingers or other shapes.

tasty tuna

55g (2oz) drained tinned tuna
  (about ⅓ tin)

1 tbsp mayonnaise

1 tsp tomato ketchup

Salt and pepper

2 slices bread, flattened

1 Put the tuna in a bowl and mash it well, then stir in the mayonnaise and ketchup. Season to taste with salt and pepper. Spread on one slice of bread and sandwich with the other slice. Cut into squares or fingers.

"cream tea"

2 tbsp cream cheese, at room temperature

2 slices bread, flattened

1½ tsp raspberry jam

1 Spread 1 tbsp of cream cheese on to each slice of bread. Spread the jam on top of one slice and top with the remaining slice. Cut into squares or fingers.

PREPARATION 5–8 MINUTES | MAKES 1–2 PORTIONS

double cheese sandwich

If your child likes **yeast extract** then you can use ¼–½ tsp instead of the ketchup. These are also nice as open-face sandwiches – just use **Cheddar cheese** and only half of the **cream cheese base.**

2 tbsp cream cheese

1½ tsp tomato ketchup

2 slices bread, flattened

30g (1oz) Cheddar cheese, thinly sliced or grated

1 Mix the cream cheese and ketchup together in a small bowl. Spread half on to each slice of bread. Top one slice with the cheese and sandwich with the remaining slice. Cut into squares or fingers.

cream cheese and banana sandwich

This is also nice **spread on toast** for breakfast.

2 tbsp cream cheese

1 tsp maple syrup (or clear honey for babies over one year)

½ small banana, mashed

2 slices bread, flattened

1 Mix the cream cheese and maple syrup (or honey) together in a bowl, then stir in the banana. Spread on to one slice of bread and sandwich with the remaining slice. Cut into squares or fingers.

PREPARATION 30 MINUTES, PLUS AT LEAST 1 HOUR CHILLING | COOKING TIME 2-3 MINUTES | MAKES ABOUT 20

broccoli and cheese baby bites

This is essentially a **broccoli and cheese purée**, bound with fresh breadcrumbs. It makes good finger food rolled into **small balls and coated in crumbs** and fried. **Chill the balls well** before cooking.

110g (4oz) broccoli florets

4 slices white bread, crusts removed

30g (1oz) mature Cheddar cheese, grated

30g (1oz) mozzarella cheese, grated

1–2 eggs, beaten

3 tbsp dried breadcrumbs

3 tbsp freshly grated Parmesan cheese

1 tbsp plain flour

3–4 tbsp sunflower oil, for frying

1 Steam the broccoli florets for 7–8 minutes until soft. Transfer them to a plate and allow to cool.

2 Put the bread in a food processor and whiz to crumbs, then tip into a bowl. Put the broccoli, Cheddar, and mozzarella in the food processor and whiz until puréed. Add to the breadcrumbs and squish everything together until well combined. (The mixture may need a little liquid to help it bind, in which case add 1–2 tsp of the beaten egg.)

3 Mix the dried breadcrumbs and Parmesan on a large plate. Put the flour on another plate and the beaten egg in a bowl. Roll teaspoonfuls of the broccoli mixture into small balls. Dust with flour, then dip in the egg and, finally, roll in the breadcrumbs. Leave to set in the fridge for at least 1 hour or, preferably, overnight.

4 Heat the oil in a non-stick frying pan and cook the balls over a high heat, turning frequently, for 2–3 minutes until golden brown all over. Drain on kitchen paper and allow to cool to warm before serving.

PREPARATION TIME 3 MINUTES | MAKES 1 BABY PORTION

banana and mango or peach

Exotic fruits such as **mango, peach, papaya, melon, and kiwi** are perfect baby foods and they don't need any cooking. Introduce them by **mixing with banana**. For older babies, a wedge of peeled mango, melon, or kiwi fruit will **make good finger foods**. All of these fruits are very nutritious.

1 small, ripe banana

½ small, ripe mango or 1 ripe peach

1 Peel the banana and mango or peach (for how to peel a peach, see page 86).

2 Mash the fruits together until quite smooth. (This purée is not suitable for freezing.)

sandwich ideas

Finger sandwiches are **good for children of all ages**, for lunch or a snack. **I like to flatten the bread** – this does make a difference for small children as they get a better ratio of filling to bread, and the sandwiches are **suited to little mouths**. Keep fillings fairly smooth.

maple-banana sandwich

★ Spread 1 tsp maple syrup over one slice of bread, then top with ½ small mashed banana. Sandwich with the second slice of bread.

avocado sandwich

★ Mash ¼ small, ripe avocado with a few drops of lemon juice. Spread over one slice of bread and sandwich with the second slice.
Variation: You could also try mixing avocado with cream cheese and chopped tomato.

cream cheese-strawberry sandwich

★ Mix 1 tbsp cream cheese with 1 tsp fruit spread or low-sugar spread. Spread over one slice of bread and sandwich with the second slice.

cheese sandwich

★ Spread the bread with a little margarine, cover with a slice of Swiss cheese, and top with the second slice of bread.
Variation: Try adding a couple of thin slices of peeled cucumber or tomato.

PREPARATION TIME: 5 MINUTES | MAKES 6–8 LOLLIES

peach melba lollies

Fresh fruit ice lollies are **great for soothing sore gums** when your **little one is teething.** They are also a great way to get more fluids into your sick child. This is a lovely combination of fruits, but these would also be **tasty made with peaches and strawberries**.

2 large, ripe peaches

175g (6oz) fresh or frozen raspberries
 (or you could use strawberries)

300ml (10fl oz) peach or apple juice

2–3 tbsp caster sugar (optional)

1 Peel the peaches (see page 86), then quarter them and remove the stones. Put the peaches and berries in a blender with half the juice and blend to a purée. Pass the purée through a sieve to remove the seeds.

2 Mix the purée with the remaining peach or apple juice and sweeten to taste with sugar, if needed.

3 Pour the purée into lolly moulds and freeze for a few hours or overnight.

PREPARATION TIME 1 MINUTE PLUS FREEZING | MAKES 4 BABY PORTIONS

far-too-easy banana ice-cream

This tastes so good that you are not going to believe how easy and quick it is to make. It's also **a fantastic, healthy alternative** to traditional ice-cream. Try it!

4 medium, ripe bananas

1 Peel the bananas, then place them on a tray that can be put into the freezer. Pop them into the freezer and leave for at least 4 hours or overnight.

2 Then simply remove the bananas from the freezer (one at a time if you want to make just one portion), cut into chunks, and whizz in a food processor until smooth.

3 If making in bulk, freeze any leftover ice-cream in a plastic box with lid. Remove a portion and allow it to soften a little before serving.

PREPARATION TIME 30 MINUTES (PLUS 30 MINUTES SOFTENING) | CUTS INTO 12–14 PORTIONS

ice-cream birthday cake

The first birthday party can be a bit of a challenge – expectations will be high. I like to surprise people by **serving an ice-cream cake** rather than the traditional birthday sponge. Your guests will be delighted, and it can be **made a couple of weeks** in advance.

Cake

2 litres (3½ pints) or 4 x 500ml (18fl oz) tubs of good-quality vanilla ice-cream or frozen vanilla yogurt, softened in the fridge for 30 minutes

500ml (18fl oz) tub raspberry sorbet, softened in the fridge for 30 minutes

Raspberry sauce

450g (1lb) fresh, or frozen and thawed, raspberries

150–200g (5½–7oz) good-quality raspberry jam (to taste)

½ tsp lemon juice

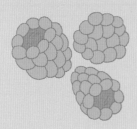

1 Put a 23cm (9in) springform cake tin in the freezer to chill. Spread half of the frozen ice-cream over the bottom of the tin and press down to level. Freeze for 10 minutes to firm up a little, then spread over a layer of sorbet, pressing level again. Freeze for 10 minutes, then top with a level layer of the remaining ice-cream. Wrap the tin tightly in foil and freeze overnight, or until needed.

2 To make the sauce, purée the raspberries with the jam and lemon juice. Sieve to remove any seeds, then cover and chill (can be made a day ahead).

3 About 45 minutes to 1 hour before serving, transfer the cake to the fridge, so it can soften slightly. Undo the spring clips on the side of the tin, lift off the side, and transfer the cake to a plate. Use a large, sharp knife to cut slices, dipping it in very hot water between each slice. Serve with the raspberry sauce spooned over.

★ **Variation:** Substitute strawberry ice-cream for the vanilla ice-cream, and serve with a warm white chocolate sauce made by melting 225g (8oz) white chocolate with 250ml (8fl oz) double cream.

chapter 4

12–18 months:
toddlers on the move

12–18 months:
what you can expect

The **transition from baby to toddler** is an exciting one for both you and your little one, and you'll find he is now capable of eating a wide variety of foods – some of them **all on his own!**

Q My toddler seems to be using mealtimes to exert her will; how can I prevent this from becoming a problem?

A Early in life, most children cotton on to the fact that their parents are concerned about how much and what they are eating. Making a fuss about food guarantees instant attention, and many children slide into the habit of using food to wield power over their parents. The best advice is to remove the pressure. If children fail to get a response, they get bored. When they realize that they won't get attention for eating badly, they'll stop using food as a tool to do so.

So, if your toddler won't eat, remove full or half-empty plates without a murmur, after around 30 minutes. Don't offer an alternative, and try not to panic too much that she hasn't eaten enough of the right foods. No child, whatever her age, will willingly starve herself, and if you continue to offer healthy food, with no pressure attached, she will eventually eat it.

Q Should my toddler be feeding himself by now?

A Most toddlers will be able to finger feed successfully at 12–18 months. They are very unlikely to manage to eat with cutlery, but they can try! Provide your toddler with his own cutlery, and encourage him to get his fingers messy, and he'll soon learn the necessary skills. The best way to approach this is to encourage him to eat with both his hands or cutlery, while you feed him at the same time. By watching you feed him, he learns the art of picking up a spoon, filling it with food, and placing it in his mouth – he'll soon be doing this himself, once he knows how.

Q Is it OK for my toddler to eat little but often?

A Some little ones can't seem to manage much at mealtimes, either because they lack the concentration necessary to sit down and finish a bowl or a plate of food, or because their tummies are small, and it takes very little to fill them up. In this case, it's fine to offer a few small meals, as long as they are all equally healthy, and not junky snacks that will fill them up with empty calories.

Q Is it necessary for my toddler to use cutlery?

A Presenting a set of "safe" and child-friendly cutlery at a young age, even if your child doesn't use it, instils the idea that cutlery accompanies mealtimes. Many little ones eat with their hands alone, which is certainly a necessary skill to develop, and perfectly acceptable in toddlerhood, but not something that should be encouraged into the preschool years.

★ tempering tantrums

Tantrums may become increasingly evident at mealtimes. A good way to bypass these is to offer a few choices in advance, so your toddler feels she has a little control. Perhaps let her choose her bowl or which vegetable she might like.

gentle weaning

Weaning is often a **tricky and emotive period** for toddlers and parents alike, as regular milk feeds are replaced with wholesome, nutritious meals. **Don't rush the process** if you aren't ready. As long as milk isn't forming the main part of your toddler's diet, you can continue to enjoy those **comforting moments**.

Q Is it OK to continue to breastfeed even when my toddler is eating a varied diet?

A There is absolutely no reason why you can't continue to breastfeed as long as both you and your toddler are enjoying it. There is plenty of research to suggest that breast milk continues to offer antibodies well into toddlerhood, which can help build up your little one's resistance to infection.

Breast milk also contains a whole host of vitamins and minerals. It is important, though, that your baby has a healthy balance between breastfeeding and solids. The majority of nutrients at this age should come from food, and not breast milk. Filling up on breast milk can lead to reduced food intake, which may lead to vitamin deficiencies.

Most importantly, perhaps, is that breastfeeding offers emotional nourishment and comfort to your child, and helps to build a healthy mother-child relationship.

Q My toddler shows no desire to stop breastfeeding, but it's starting to get embarrassing. What do you recommend?

A If you are feeling pressured because you are breastfeeding past the point at which many mums give up, try limiting it to morning and evening feeds, when you can feed in private. If you are ready to give up altogether, take it slowly. Start by losing one feed at a time and offer a drink or snack in its place. It can take time, but weaning needs to happen sometime.

Q Should I stop the night-time bottle?

A It is easy to fall into the habit of offering a night-time bottle because it's comforting. The longer this goes on, the harder it is to stop, and drinking from a bottle at night can play havoc with children's teeth (see page 129). It's a good idea to offer a cup instead. However, if you're finding it hard to get your toddler away from his bottle, gradually water down his evening bottle over a few weeks, until it is virtually tasteless, and encourage other comfort items, such as a favourite toy. See box, right, to ensure he gets his calcium requirements though.

Q My child doesn't seem to like water. How can I make it more appealing?

A If your toddler is used to sweet drinks and milk, water probably does seem boring. Buy her a water bottle, perhaps with her favourite character on it, and keep it topped up throughout the day, so she gets into the habit of drinking whenever she is thirsty. Sometimes offering water with some ice cubes and a straw can make it more fun, too. If this doesn't work, try adding a tiny bit of juice or high-fruit squash and then reducing the flavouring little by little until she's drinking water alone.

Q Does it matter if my child won't drink any milk?

A Lots of children can't or won't drink milk, and grow and develop perfectly well. The most important element of milk is calcium, which is required for healthy bones and teeth. Calcium is found in all dairy produce, so if he's eating yogurt, fromage frais, and cheese, he's probably getting enough. Leafy-green vegetables are also a good source of calcium, and use milk when you can in cooking: in rice pudding, creamy or cheese sauces, or even mashed potatoes or other root vegetables.

Q Should my toddler be drinking her milk from a cup?

A It's a good idea to wean your baby on to a cup by the age of 6–12 months, when the sucking reflex is replaced by an ability to sip and swallow. A cup is less damaging to her teeth as the sucking action when drinking from a bottle causes milk to "swirl" around the mouth, bathing the teeth in the natural sugars that it contains. A cup will also limit her association of milk with comfort, which can sometimes lead to problems with comfort eating and weight problems later on – and also difficulties settling without a bottle. Start by switching the teat on her bottle to a "spout", so that she becomes used to drinking rather than sucking. Then buy a few brightly coloured beakers and ask her to choose the one she'd like to have her milk or water in. If she feels that she's got some power to choose, the disappointment of not having a bottle will soon be forgotten.

★ did you know ...

that children over the age of one should get about 570ml milk (1 pint) a day? Remember, though, that this is to provide the total amount of calcium required, so if your toddler has a yogurt or two, some cheese, and milk on her cereal, she'll need correspondingly less. In fact, a glass of milk a day, plus a yogurt and a small piece of cheese is actually just about right for most toddlers, even though it's tempting to offer more than this.

learning to love food

Your toddler needs plenty of variety and lots of different nutrients from fresh, natural foods. **Encourage your little one** to try new foods regularly, and to enjoy versions of healthy family meals, and she'll soon be on her way to **establishing healthy eating patterns** – and learning to love great food!

Q What does a varied "toddler" diet mean?

A A varied diet includes a variety of different foods. We know that kids need the basics of protein, carbohydrates, fats, and vitamins and minerals, and the best way to ensure that they get what they need is to offer as many different foods as often as possible.

★ mix and match

The wider the range of foods you offer the better. Wheat-based pastas or breads offer a good source of carbohydrates, but also include different forms, such as rice, potatoes, and different grains (buckwheat, oats, etc.) from time to time. Offer vegetarian proteins such as tofu or pulses at one meal, and fish or chicken at the next. Experiment with the whole spectrum of brightly coloured fruit and vegetables, ensuring you toddler gets all the key nutrients she needs.

Q How many servings of carbohydrates does my toddler need each day?

A Try to ensure that every meal has at least one or two servings of carbohydrates, and that your child has at least one or two carb-rich snacks as well. Add a little mashed potato, some couscous, pasta, quinoa, or rice to his main meal, alongside fresh vegetables (which are also rich in carbohydrates). Also offer toast, porridge, or cereal with breakfast, and perhaps some breadsticks and fresh fruit at snacktime. Sandwiches, pasta dishes, risottos, and jacket potatoes are also high in carbohydrates.

Q Are there any grains that are too harsh for my toddler's digestion?

A Wholegrains such as brown rice, wild rice, quinoa, oats, millet, and corn are good sources of protein, carbohydrates, vitamins, minerals, and fibre, and are a great addition to a toddler's diet. It is, however, better to stick to small portions as they are rich in fibre and can fill up little tummies very quickly. Too much fibre increases the speed at which foods are digested, which can lead to inadequate intake of some nutrients.

Q How can I persuade my toddler to eat meat?

A Often it's the texture rather than the taste of the meat that toddlers object to. Minced meat is good for little ones; make sure you choose lean mince. When making dishes such as bolognese or shepherd's pie, I often brown the minced meat and then chop it for a few seconds in a blender, so it has a less lumpy texture. Combining a tasty minced meat with a mashed potato and carrot topping, or mixing it with pasta, are other good ways to make it easier to eat.

You can also encourage your toddler to enjoy eating meat by making mini meatballs that he can pick up with his fingers. My recipe for Chicken meatballs on pages 182–83 contains sautéed red onion, carrot, and apple, so is very tasty and appealing to little children. Meatballs can also be made using minced beef. Also consider adding tiny pieces of meat to pastas or risottos, where they aren't quite so overwhelming.

If your child is still resistant to eating meat, don't despair. Pulses such as chickpeas, butter beans, kidney beans, peas, and lentils can all be added to soups, stews, casseroles, or pasta dishes to provide a good source of protein; they can even be offered on their own, as they are easy for little fingers to manage. Rice and wholegrains, such as barley, wheat, buckwheat, corn, and oats, are also high in protein, as are nut butters or ground nuts, seeds and quinoa, which can be eaten on their own, or added to your child's favourite dish.

A little hummus with some wholegrain toast, for example, is a good protein-based snack. Don't forget, too, that eggs and dairy produce are as high in protein as meat, so a scrambled egg with a little grated cheese will be a perfect high-protein meal.

Q Do toddlers need five servings of fruit and vegetables every day?

A Toddlers need at least five servings of fruit and vegetables a day, but it doesn't need to be as daunting as it sounds! At this age, a serving is roughly what your toddler can hold in her hand. So a couple of grapes, a few pieces of apple, or a tablespoon of sweetcorn or peas will count as one serving. Vegetables blended into pasta sauces, and hidden in dishes such as spinach and ricotta lasagne or butternut squash risotto, are other good ways to get your toddler to eat her veggies. Potato doesn't count, but sweet potato and carrots do, so mash potato with these as a topping for cottage pie.

A handful of berries or dried fruit, such as raisins or apricots, make good snacks, and you can sprinkle porridge or breakfast cereal with fresh berries. A small glass of fruit juice or a smoothie also count as a serving. Homemade fresh fruit ice lollies are another tasty way to get your little one to eat more fruit (see my lolly recipe on page 120).

Brightly coloured fruits and vegetables are best for your child as the pigment contains antioxidants, so make sure there is plenty of colour on your child's plate.

independent eating

Finger foods aren't just snacks or incidental additions to your toddler's diet. You can supplement even the faddiest toddler's menu with **appealing goodies** that will both add nutritional value and encourage her to learn the **skills of independent eating**.

Q How can I encourage my child to eat foods with different consistencies?

A Some little ones find the transition from purées to lumps, and then to mashed, chopped, and cut food more difficult than others, and may be reluctant to eat meals that require chewing. In some cases, it comes down to laziness, or it may be that weaning took place a little later than usual.

It is important that you continue to introduce foods with different textures. One of the best ways to do this is to offer what is effectively a balanced selection of finger foods at every meal, so everything he eats must be chewed, with no purées at all. For example, peas, sweet potato cubes, strips of chicken, and chunks of steamed new potatoes, or a pot of rice with fish balls and steamed broccoli. Many children seem to find it easier to move straight on to this "real food", rather than progressing through different textures.

Q How small should I mash or chop foods for my toddler?

A Once your toddler has some teeth, she can manage most soft foods that have been diced, grated, or mashed. In fact even without teeth it is surprising what a set of gums can munch their way through. Certainly by 12 to 18 months, your toddler should be able to enjoy a variety of different finger foods, which can be incorporated into his regular meals. As long as the food isn't too tough, which may be beyond the capabilities of little teeth and gums, small pieces of most foods can be managed easily. If your child gags or has trouble managing diced foods, try making the pieces a little smaller until he's more adept at chewing. I often find it useful to whiz tougher cuts of meat in a grinder for a few seconds, to smooth out some of the lumps and bumps, and make them a little softer for little ones. Use your "ground" meats as a base for any meat dish, including pasta sauces, casseroles, or dishes such as Chicken meatballs (pages 182–83) and Funny-face beef burgers (page 181). You can also try increasing the chunks in the foods that he already loves and is most familiar with, where they will not be so readily noticed or identified!

Q My toddler still refuses to eat anything with lumps – what can I do?

A Some babies and toddlers, particularly those who have been weaned onto jarred baby foods, tend to like things smooth! They can often develop the most amazing ability to filter out every single lump and spit them out. Some little ones simply gag because it's taken them a little longer to develop the knack of chewing things well enough to make them easily swallowed. You should visit your doctor, however, if your toddler regularly gags or refuses lumps, as there may be a physical cause at the root.

There are a few ways you can help your child to accept lumpy food. First of all, don't force it. If your toddler senses that you are angry or anxious, he'll begin to find the whole experience of eating traumatic, and may literally gag or choke on even the tiniest lumps because he feels under pressure.

Slowly increase the lumpiness of his food, and allow him to play messily with it. Babies and toddlers tend to prefer overall lumpiness to something smooth with the occasional lump, so pasta stirred into a favourite purée is a good way to introduce more texture.

Also offer finger foods alongside his meals. Start with soft foods, such as steamed carrots and broccoli or avocado, and move on to slightly harder foods, such as toast fingers and well-cooked pasta shapes, before he's comfortable with chewing, when you can introduce cubes of soft cheese, dried apricots, and chunks of meat, for example.

Once your toddler starts to experiment a little and becomes more comfortable with lumps, it's a good idea to encourage him to stir "lumpy" ingredients into his foods, such as raisins into cereal, or to dip finger foods into purées. Over time, all will be well.

Q What are the best finger foods for this age group?

A Incorporating as many different food groups as you can will make a big difference to the number of nutrients your toddler gets. Raw vegetables, such as carrot sticks, cucumber, or strips of red pepper, are often more popular than cooked. Try some more unusual vegetables, too. Crunchy sugar snap peas are delicious – serve them with hummus. Berries, grapes, mango, apple, and banana are all healthy snacks. You can also make fresh fruit ice lollies by blending fruits together with fruit juice or yogurt and freezing in mini ice-lolly moulds – chewing on something cold will also help relieve your toddler's sore gums. For wholesome carbohydrates, choose breadsticks, wholemeal toast fingers, finger sandwiches, flapjacks, rice cakes, healthy breakfast cereals, and well-cooked pasta. As long as there is no risk of choking, anything goes!

★ finger food dips

Make a dip for dipping vegetable batons by blending together 125g (4½oz) cottage cheese, 2 tbsp mayonnaise, a heaped tbsp tomato ketchup, and a squeeze of lemon juice. For a more fruity dip, blend together a little cottage cheese with some sugar, a few drops of vanilla, and some apricot purée.

PREPARATION TIME 10 MINUTES | COOKING TIME 15 MINUTES | MAKES 2 CHILD PORTIONS

rainbow pasta

When learning to feed themselves, toddlers can get frustrated with a spoon and fork and **prefer to use their fingers**, so pasta dishes that are not too "slippery" are ideal. This one includes a delicious and **colourful range of vegetables** – you can both have fun identifying the colours as your toddler eats.

85g (3oz) pasta shapes

½ carrot, peeled and cut into matchsticks

2 broccoli florets, cut in small pieces

2 tsp olive oil

½ yellow courgette, halved lengthways and sliced

¼ small red pepper, deseeded and cut into matchsticks

3 tbsp crème fraîche

55g (2oz) Cheddar cheese (medium or mild, according to preference), grated

2 tbsp grated Parmesan cheese

1 Cook the pasta in boiling water according to packet instructions, adding the carrot and broccoli for the last 3 minutes of the cooking time.

2 Meanwhile, heat the oil in a large frying pan or wok and stir-fry the courgette and red pepper for 3–4 minutes until softened and lightly golden.

3 Drain the pasta, carrots, and broccoli and add to the frying pan. Add the crème fraîche and cheeses. Toss everything together over a low heat for about 1 minute to heat the crème fraîche and just melt the cheeses. Serve warm. (This dish is not suitable for reheating.)

PREPARATION TIME 15 MINUTES | COOKING TIME 4–6 MINUTES | MAKES 6–8 CHILD PORTIONS

fish goujons

Toddlers can be **notoriously faddy** about fish, but most like these **baby-sized fish fingers** made with tender white fish. While they're perfect for little hands, **the whole family** will enjoy them too.

45g (1½oz) dried breadcrumbs

30g (1oz) Parmesan cheese, grated

¼ tsp paprika (optional)

Freshly ground black pepper

1 egg

1 tsp water

2 tbsp plain flour

225g (8oz) fresh white fish fillet, such as cod or sole, cut into little finger-sized strips (if you are planning to freeze the goujons, be sure the fish has not previously been frozen)

3–4 tbsp sunflower oil, for frying

1 Mix together the breadcrumbs, Parmesan, and paprika (if using) and season with pepper. Spread the crumb mixture out on a large plate.

2 Beat the egg in a bowl with the water. Spread the flour out on another large plate.

3 Coat the fish pieces in the flour, then dip in the egg and coat in the breadcrumbs. If planning to freeze, lay the coated fish goujons on a baking sheet lined with baking parchment. If cooking immediately, put them on a plate.

4 Heat the oil in a large frying pan over a moderate heat. Fry the fish goujons for 2–3 minutes on each side until they are golden and the fish is just cooked through. Drain on kitchen paper. Check the temperature before serving.

5 To freeze (uncooked), cover the baking sheet with cling film and freeze for 2–3 hours until the fish is firm. Transfer to a sealable plastic bag or box and store in the freezer. Cook from frozen, adding about 30 seconds per side extra cooking time.

PREPARATION TIME 5 MINUTES | COOKING TIME 10 MINUTES | MAKES 1 CHILD PORTION

cheese and ham pit-zas

Pittas make a **nice crisp base for pizzas** – or pit-zas! Try my tomato sauce on page 179 or use a good-quality store-bought sauce. If you only have large pittas, **then warm and split one** as described in the recipe, and just use one half. Another good base for a pizza is a **split toasted muffin.** For a vegetarian version, leave out the ham.

1 small, round pitta bread (about 8cm/3in diameter)

2 tbsp tomato sauce

30g (1oz) mozzarella or Cheddar cheese, grated

½ thin slice of ham, cut into thin strips

1 tsp sliced black olives (optional)

2–3 fresh basil leaves, to garnish (optional)

1 Preheat the oven to 200°C (180°C fan), gas 6.

2 Warm the pitta bread in a microwave for about 10 seconds, then carefully split in half to give two thin rounds. Place the pitta halves on a baking sheet, crumb side up. Spread tomato sauce over the rounds and scatter on the cheese, ham, and olives, if using.

3 Bake for 9–10 minutes until the cheese has melted and the pitta is crisp. Cool slightly before cutting each pit-za into four. Scatter a little torn basil on top to garnish, if you like.

★ **Variations:** Toast the pitta halves under the grill, then add the toppings and continue cooking under the grill until the cheese melts. For hungry toddlers or older children, use a whole mini pitta.

packed lunch ideas

If your child is in a nursery or daycare facility that requires a packed lunch, or **you're out and about**, it can be difficult to come up with ideas. Here are some great lunches that cover all the **requirements for a balanced meal**.

lunchbox 1
- Cheese or ham sandwiches (cut into fun shapes) or mini bagels
- Carrot and cucumber sticks
- Pitta bread fingers with hummus
- Yogurt
- Apple slices and halved grapes
- Smoothie or 100 per cent juice

lunchbox 2
- Cheese slices cut into shapes plus strips of ham packed into pots
- Mini rice cakes or unsalted crackers (lightly butter them first, if you like)
- Blueberries or quartered grapes
- Oat and raisin cookie (or yogurt/ fromage frais)

lunchbox 3
- Tuna mini sub – fill a split hot dog bun with 30g (1oz) drained canned tuna, 2 tsp Greek yogurt, ½ tsp tomato ketchup, 2–3 drops of lemon juice, and ¼ tsp sweet chilli sauce (optional)
- Carrot sticks
- Cottage cheese and pineapple pot (or yogurt)

lunchbox 4
- Cream cheese and fruit wrap – spread 1–2 tbsp cream cheese over a flour tortilla and scatter on small pieces of dried apricots or add a thin layer of good-quality fruit spread. Roll up and cut into 3–4 pieces.
- Cucumber sticks
- Mini muffin (or yogurt/fromage frais)

lunchbox 5
- Peanut butter on mini bagel
- Creamy potato salad with chopped ham or chicken
- Apple slices

lunchbox 6
- Cheese sandwich on wholegrain bread
- Melon and strawberry salad (cut into bite-sized pieces)
- Yogurt

lunchbox 7
- Pasta salad with chicken, lightly cooked broccoli, and sweetcorn, and a dressing made with 1½ tbsp light olive oil and ½ tbsp each of honey, soy sauce, and lemon juice
- Probiotic yogurt drink
- Mini pack of dried fruit
- Cereal bar or fruity muffin

PREPARATION TIME 10 MINUTES | COOKING TIME 13–17 MINUTES | SERVES A FAMILY OF 4–5

pesto pasta with chicken and cherry tomatoes

Children seem to love pesto, even those who shy away from green foods! **Making your own is easy and it keeps very well**, although you can use 100g (3½oz) pesto from a jar instead. Vegetarians can replace the chicken **with cubed fresh mozzarella.**

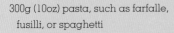

300g (10oz) pasta, such as farfalle, fusilli, or spaghetti

30g (1oz) bunch of fresh basil, stems discarded

½ garlic clove

30g (1oz) pine nuts, lightly toasted

6 tbsp olive oil, plus 1 tsp extra

30g (1oz) Parmesan cheese, grated, plus extra to serve

Salt and freshly ground black pepper

1–2 tbsp boiling water

115g (4oz) cherry tomatoes, halved

175g (6oz) cooked chicken, shredded

1 Cook the pasta in boiling water according to the packet instructions. Meanwhile, make the pesto. Put the basil leaves in a food processor with the garlic. Process to a purée, then add the pine nuts and process until the nuts are finely chopped, stopping and scraping down the sides of the processor bowl as necessary. Keep the motor running and trickle 6 tbsp of the olive oil into the processor. When all the oil is mixed in, add the Parmesan and salt and pepper to taste, and pulse three or four times to combine. Add just enough boiling water to thin slightly.

2 Drain the pasta and set aside. Put the extra 1 tsp oil in the empty pasta pan and add the tomatoes. Fry them gently for 2–3 minutes until just softening. Add the pesto and chicken and heat through for 1–2 minutes (the chicken must be piping hot). Add the cooked, drained pasta and toss everything together. Spoon on to serving plates and serve with extra Parmesan.

PREPARATION TIME 1 HOUR | COOKING TIME 35–40 MINUTES | SERVES A FAMILY OF 4–5

lasagne al forno

Nothing is more of **a crowd-pleaser** than a big dish of baked lasagne – at any age and any time of year! Mixing the meat and cheese sauces may sound odd, but **it makes the sauce taste richer.**

1 tbsp olive oil, plus extra to grease

1 red onion, chopped

1 carrot, peeled and grated

55g (2oz) chestnut mushrooms, chopped

1 garlic clove, crushed

400g (14oz) can chopped tomatoes

4 tbsp tomato purée

2 tbsp tomato ketchup

450g (1lb) lean minced beef

150ml (5fl oz) beef stock

1 tsp soft light brown sugar

¼ tsp dried oregano

9 sheets no-precook lasagne

85g (3oz) mozzarella cheese, grated

30g (1oz) grated Parmesan cheese

Cheese sauce

4 tbsp cornflour

600ml (1 pint) milk

115g (4oz) mascarpone

Freshly grated nutmeg

1 Heat the oil in a large, deep frying pan and cook the vegetables gently until soft and lightly browned. Add the garlic and cook for 1 minute. Transfer the vegetables to a blender and add the tomatoes, tomato purée, and ketchup. Blend until smooth.

2 Brown the mince in the pan, then add the tomato mixture, beef stock, sugar, and oregano. Simmer for about 30 minutes or until thick. Season to taste.

3 Make the cheese sauce by mixing the cornflour in a saucepan with a little of the milk until smooth. Whisk in the remaining milk. Bring to the boil and cook, whisking, for 1 minute or until thick. Remove from the heat and stir in the mascarpone. Season to taste with nutmeg, salt, and pepper.

4 Lightly oil a large rectangular ovenproof dish (about 28 x 18cm/11 x 7in). Mix half of the cheese sauce into the meat sauce. Spread 2 tbsp of the remaining cheese sauce over the bottom of the dish, then put on a layer of three lasagne sheets. Spoon over half of the meat mixture, then add another layer of pasta. Spoon over the remaining meat mixture and top with a final layer of pasta. Cover with the remaining cheese sauce and scatter the grated cheeses over the surface.

5 Preheat the oven to 190°C (170°C fan), gas 5. Bake
the lasagne for 35–40 minutes until golden brown
on top and cooked through. Test by inserting a
knife down through the centre; you should feel no
resistance. Leave to stand for 10 minutes before
cutting and serving.

6 The unbaked lasagne can be kept in the fridge,
covered, until needed (up to 24 hours ahead). It
can also be frozen, wrapped well in foil; thaw in
the fridge for 24 hours. To bake a chilled or thawed
lasagne, preheat the oven to 180°C (160°C fan), gas
4. Bake for 40 minutes, then increase the oven to
200°C (180°C fan), gas 6 and bake for a further 10
minutes or until golden brown on top and piping
hot. Leave to stand for 10 minutes before serving.

PREPARATION TIME 10 MINUTES | COOKING TIME 1 HOUR 35 MINUTES | MAKES 4–6 SMALL PIES

vegetarian shepherd's pie

Lentils are a **good source of protein and iron** for vegetarians, and green lentils in a tomato sauce makes a **savoury and satisfying filling** for these little potato-topped pies.

1 tbsp olive oil

1 red onion, finely chopped

1 carrot, peeled and grated

1 garlic clove, crushed

150g (5½oz) green lentils, rinsed

400g (14oz) can chopped tomatoes

600ml (1 pint) vegetable stock

150ml (5fl oz) water

2 tbsp tomato purée

1 tbsp soy sauce

1 tbsp soft light brown sugar

Freshly ground black pepper

5 tbsp frozen peas (optional)

Topping

750g (1lb 10oz) potatoes, peeled and
    cut in chunks

20g (¾oz) butter

4 tbsp milk

Beaten egg or grated Cheddar cheese

1 Heat the oil in a large saucepan and sauté the onion and carrot until softened and lightly browned. Add the garlic and cook for 1 minute. Stir in the lentils, tomatoes, stock, water, tomato purée, soy sauce, and sugar. Bring to the boil, then reduce the heat, part-cover, and simmer for about 1 hour or until the lentils are tender.

2 Meanwhile, cook the potatoes in lightly salted boiling water for about 15 minutes or until tender. Drain, then mash well with the butter and milk.

3 Season the lentils to taste with pepper and stir in the peas, if using. Divide among 4–6 ramekins or other small baking dishes. Spread the mashed potato over the lentils and mark in ridges with a fork. Cool, then chill. Or wrap in cling film and freeze; thaw overnight in the fridge when needed.

4 To cook, preheat the oven to 200°C (180°C fan), gas 6. Put the pies on a baking sheet, brush the tops with beaten egg (or sprinkle with cheese), and bake for about 30 minutes or until golden and piping hot. Allow to cool slightly and check the temperature before serving.

PREPARATION 30 MINUTES | COOKING TIME 20-25 MINUTES | MAKES 4-6 INDIVIDUAL PIES

first fish pie

To **make the purée from scratch**, you need to steam 90g (generous 3oz) peeled and cubed butternut squash for 8–10 minutes until soft, then mash or **whiz in a blender or food processor**.

250g (9oz) skinless cod fillet (or similar white fish), cubed

Topping

500g (1lb 2oz) potatoes, peeled and cubed

15g (½oz) butter

3 tbsp milk

Salt and pepper

Sauce

10g (⅓oz) butter

10g (⅓oz) plain flour

150ml (5fl oz) milk

80g (scant 3oz) butternut squash purée (see above)

55g (2oz) mature Cheddar cheese, grated

2 tbsp freshly grated Parmesan cheese

1 Divide the cubed fish among four to six small ovenproof ramekins. Cook the potatoes in boiling salted water for about 15 minutes until just tender. Drain the potatoes, and mash. Beat in the butter and milk, and season to taste.

2 While the potatoes are cooking, melt the butter in a small saucepan, then stir in the flour and cook for 1 minute. Remove from the heat and gradually stir in the milk until you have a smooth sauce. Return to a low heat and cook, stirring constantly, until the sauce comes to the boil and thickens. Stir in the squash purée, then remove from the heat and stir in the cheeses until melted. Cool slightly before spooning over the fish.

3 Preheat the oven to 200°C (180°C fan), gas 6. Spoon the mashed potatoes over the fish and sauce, and mark the surface with ridges using a fork.

4 Set the dish(es) on a baking tray and bake for 20 minutes until hot in the centre and golden on top. If the pies are fridge-cold, bake them for an extra 5 minutes. The tops can be browned further under a hot grill, if you like.

PREPARATION 10–15 MINUTES | COOKING TIME 30 MINUTES | MAKES 4 PORTIONS

chicken parmigiana

I would **defy even the fussiest child** to reject this **dish as it ticks** all of the right boxes for **baby tastebuds.**

1 large shallot, diced

1 tbsp olive oil

1 small clove garlic, crushed

1 x 400g (14oz) tin chopped tomatoes

1½ tbsp tomato purée

1 tsp sugar

Salt and pepper

2 x 140g (5oz) skinless, boneless chicken breasts

1 egg, beaten

2 tbsp plain flour

55g (2oz) dried breadcrumbs

3–4 tbsp sunflower oil, for frying

55g (2oz) mozzarella cheese, grated

2 tbsp freshly grated Parmesan cheese

1 Put the shallot and olive oil in a large pan and sauté for 4–5 minutes until soft. Add the garlic and cook for 1 minute, then stir in the tomatoes, tomato purée, and sugar. Simmer for 20–25 minutes until thick. Season to taste. Remove from the heat and blend to a purée. Keep warm.

2 While the sauce is simmering, cut the chicken breasts in half horizontally and lay each half out flat. Cover with cling film and beat until about 5mm (¼in) thick. Put the egg in a bowl; spread the flour on a plate; spread the breadcrumbs on a second plate and season them. Dust the chicken breast halves with flour, then dip in the egg, and, finally, coat with the breadcrumbs.

3 Heat the sunflower oil in a large non-stick frying pan and cook the chicken breasts over a medium heat for about 3 minutes on each side until the coating is golden brown and the chicken is just cooked. Drain briefly on kitchen paper and transfer to an ovenproof dish. Preheat the grill to high.

4 Spread about 3 tbsp of tomato sauce over each chicken breast and scatter over the mozzarella and Parmesan. Grill for 3–4 minutes until the cheese is bubbling. Cool slightly before serving.

PREPARATION 5 MINUTES | COOKING TIME 12-15 MINUTES | MAKES 1 PORTION

cheese and peas orzo

Orzo, which is small rice-shaped pasta, is **easy to swallow** and **good for smaller children** (use stelline or other small pasta shapes if you cannot get orzo). This dish is **quite "sticky" when cooked,** so is useful for toddlers who are trying to use a spoon or fork – there's **a good chance some will stay** on the utensil and reach the mouth!

2 tbsp orzo

1 tbsp frozen peas (petits pois if possible)

1 tbsp crème fraîche or double cream

20g (¾oz) Cheddar cheese, finely grated

1 tsp freshly grated Parmesan cheese

1 Cook the orzo according to packet instructions (you can use vegetable stock instead of water for more flavour). Add the peas for the final minute of cooking. Drain well and return the orzo and peas to the saucepan over a low heat.

2 Stir in the crème fraîche and bubble for a couple of minutes until almost fully absorbed. Remove from the heat and stir in the Cheddar until melted. Cool slightly to warm before serving with the Parmesan.

PREPARATION 5–10 MINUTES | COOKING TIME 8–10 MINUTES | MAKES 1 PORTION

quick chicken risotto

If you are **in a real hurry** then you can omit the **shallot and broccoli** and just add 1 tbsp peas with the chicken.

1 tsp butter

1 tsp finely diced shallot

45g (1½oz) small broccoli florets

55g (2oz) cooked rice

4 tbsp chicken stock

30g (1oz) cooked chicken, shredded
  (see page 108)

1 tbsp freshly grated Parmesan cheese

1 Melt the butter in a small saucepan and sauté the shallot for 5–6 minutes until soft. Meanwhile, steam the broccoli for 3–4 minutes until just tender.

2 Add the rice, stock, chicken, and cooked broccoli to the saucepan and simmer for 2–3 minutes until most of the stock has been absorbed. Remove from the heat and stir in the Parmesan.

PREPARATION 15–20 MINUTES, PLUS 8 HOURS MARINATING | COOKING TIME 6 MINUTES | MAKES 16

crunchy tofu cubes

Tofu is a good source of protein and its fairly soft texture makes it a good food for babies with few teeth. **Vegans can omit the flour and egg part of the coating and just roll the marinated tofu cubes in breadcrumbs. However, you will need to cook the crumbed tofu immediately as the crumbs will go soggy if left standing. Also, the cubes will be a bit softer** and less easy to pick up than the egg and breadcrumbed version. Note that **this recipe is for toddlers** over one year – salt in soy sauce is unsuitable for younger children.

250g (9oz) extra firm tofu, cut into 2cm (¾in) cubes

½ tsp grated fresh root ginger

2 tsp soy sauce

1 tsp mirin

1 tsp clear honey

2 tbsp plain flour

1 egg, lightly beaten

30g (1oz) dried breadcrumbs (preferably honey panko)

5 tbsp sunflower oil, for frying

1 Blot as much excess liquid as possible from the tofu cubes, using kitchen paper. Mix the ginger, soy sauce, mirin, and honey together in a bowl. Add the tofu and toss to coat, then cover and marinate in the fridge for 8 hours, or overnight, turning the cubes once or twice.

2 Put the flour and egg in separate bowls and spread the breadcrumbs on a large plate. Remove the tofu cubes from the marinade, then dust with flour, dip in egg, and roll in breadcrumbs.

3 Put a thin layer of oil in a large non-stick frying pan and heat until shimmering. Drop a couple of breadcrumbs into the oil – if they sizzle straight away, the oil is hot enough. Fry the tofu cubes for 30–40 seconds on each side until golden brown all over. Drain on kitchen paper and allow to cool until warm before serving. Or serve cold.

PREPARATION TIME 10 MINUTES | COOKING TIME 15 MINUTES | SERVES A FAMILY OF 4–5

grilled chicken yakitori

I find that grilled skewers of **chicken thigh** are more tender and moist than chicken breast, and this yakitori glaze is delicious. **These skewers** would also be **great cooked on a barbecue.**

4 fairly large skinless, boneless
   chicken thighs

4 spring onions

4 small bamboo skewers, soaked in
   water for at least 20 minutes

2–3 tbsp sunflower oil

Yakitori glaze

3 tbsp soy sauce

3 tbsp mirin (sweet Japanese rice wine)

3 tbsp clear honey

2 tsp rice vinegar

1 tsp grated fresh root ginger

1 small garlic clove, crushed

1 To make the glaze, combine all the ingredients in a small saucepan and bring to the boil. Reduce the heat to moderate and simmer, stirring occasionally, for about 5 minutes or until reduced to a fairly thick and syrupy glaze.

2 While the glaze cooks, trim away the excess fat from the chicken thighs. Cut each thigh into three pieces – they'll be about 2cm (¾in) wide. Cut each spring onion into three pieces.

3 Preheat the grill and line the grill rack with foil. Open out the pieces of chicken and thread concertina-fashion on to the soaked skewers, alternating with the spring onions. You should have three pieces of each on a skewer. Place on the foil and brush all over with oil.

4 Grill for about 5 minutes on each side, then turn the skewers and brush with half the glaze. Grill for 3 minutes, then turn over again and brush with the remaining glaze. Grill for a final 2–3 minutes or until the chicken is cooked through.

5 Remove the chicken from the skewers and serve, with the cooking juices spooned over if you like.

PREPARATION TIME 10 MINUTES | COOKING TIME 3 HOURS | MAKES 6–8 CHILD PORTIONS, DEPENDING ON APPETITE

mummy's chicken soup

Even if chicken soup doesn't have any proven medical benefits, a **bowlful of golden broth** is enough to comfort anyone who is feeling under the weather. **I like to add extra vegetables**, but if your child isn't keen, leave them out and serve this as chicken noodle soup.

2 chicken portions, trimmed of visible fat

1 onion, quartered

1 large carrot, peeled and cut into 4 chunks

1 parsnip, cut into 4 chunks (optional)

1 large leek, halved and washed

½ outer celery stick

1 garlic clove, peeled but left whole

3 sprigs of fresh thyme or a few parsley stalks plus 1 small bay leaf (or a bouquet garni)

5 black peppercorns

1.2 litres (2 pints) water

1 chicken or vegetable stock cube (optional)

2 tbsp frozen or canned naturally sweet sweetcorn in water, drained

2 tbsp frozen peas

30g (1oz) fine egg noodles or vermicelli

1 Put the chicken portions in a large saucepan. Add the onion, carrot, parsnip (if using), leek, celery, garlic, herbs, and peppercorns. Pour over the water and add the stock cube (if using). Bring to the boil, skimming off any froth with a slotted spoon, then reduce the heat to low, cover, and simmer very gently for 1¼ hours.

2 Strain the chicken broth into a clean pan. Reserve the chicken, carrot, and parsnip (if using); discard the remaining contents of the sieve.

3 Bring the broth back to the boil. Add the sweetcorn and peas, and crumble in the noodles. Cook for 3 minutes. Meanwhile, pull the chicken meat from the bones, discarding the skin; chop the meat. Dice the reserved carrot and parsnip. Add these to the soup. Taste and season, if necessary. Allow to cool slightly before serving.

4 The soup can be stored in the fridge for 2 days. Or freeze for up to 1 month (I prefer to freeze it without the peas and sweetcorn and add these when reheating); thaw overnight in the fridge. Reheat until boiling. Cool slightly before serving.

PREPARATION TIME 5 MINUTES | COOKING TIME 25 MINUTES | MAKES ABOUT 8 CHILD PORTIONS

honey, oat, and raisin crisp

Oats make a good breakfast cereal as they contain **slow-burn carbohydrates** that help to keep blood sugar levels on an even keel until snack time. Serve this with **milk and delicious fresh berries** to tempt even the fussiest little eater.

175g (6oz) rolled oats

15g (½oz) desiccated coconut

Pinch of salt

55g (2oz) soft light brown sugar

2 tbsp sunflower oil, plus a little extra for greasing

2 tbsp clear honey

1 tsp vanilla extract

55g (2oz) raisins

30g (1oz) sunflower seeds (optional)

To serve

Milk and fresh berries

1 Preheat the oven to 160°C (140°C fan), gas 3.

2 Put the oats in a large bowl and stir in the coconut, salt, and sugar. Whisk together the oil, honey, and vanilla extract and pour over the oats. Stir until the oats are evenly coated, then spread out in a lightly oiled baking tray.

3 Bake for about 25 minutes or until golden and crisp, stirring several times. Watch carefully towards the end of the cooking time to make sure the oats don't burn. Cool on the baking tray, then mix in the raisins and sunflower seeds, if using. Store in an airtight container.

4 Serve each portion (about 2 tbsp, depending on appetite) with cold milk and topped with berries.

PREPARATION TIME 10 MINUTES | COOKING TIME 20 MINUTES | MAKES 16 BARS OR 20 SQUARES

fruity flapjacks

Active children need to have **regular snacks**, particularly toddlers who can be **so busy with life** in general that it is often difficult to get them to stop for regular meals. The oats in these flapjacks will provide **long-lasting energy**. For a plain flapjack, leave out the raisins and sultanas.

100g (3½oz) butter

115g (4oz) soft light brown sugar

2 tbsp golden syrup

225g (8oz) rolled oats

30g (1oz) raisins

30g (1oz) sultanas

30g (1oz) dried cranberries (optional)

¼ tsp salt

1 egg, beaten

1 tsp vanilla extract

1 Preheat the oven to 180°C (160°C fan), gas 4. Line an 28 x 18cm (11 x 7in) shallow baking tin with baking parchment; cut the paper so it is large enough to extend above the sides of the tin.

2 Put the butter, sugar, and golden syrup in a saucepan and heat gently, stirring occasionally, until the butter and sugar have melted. Set aside to cool slightly.

3 Combine the oats, fruits, and salt in a large bowl. Add the egg, vanilla extract, and cooled butter mixture and mix together well. Spoon into the prepared tin and spread out evenly. Press down firmly with a potato masher or the back of the spoon (or your fingers). Bake for about 20 minutes or until golden brown and firm to the touch.

4 Leave to cool in the tin, then lift out using the baking parchment. Cut into bars or squares and store in an airtight container.

PREPARATION TIME 15 MINUTES | MAKES 4

blueberry-lime cheesecakes

This dessert is **ideal for little ones** as it makes small, individual cheesecakes. They are **fun to make with your child** – he can help crush the biscuits, mix the filling, and put the fruit on top. A ginger **biscuit base and raspberries** are nice alternatives.

85g (3oz) digestive biscuits

45g (1½oz) butter, melted

55g (2oz) cream cheese, at room temperature

4 tbsp Greek yogurt

Grated zest and juice of 1 lime

30g (1oz) icing sugar, sifted

100ml (3½fl oz) double cream

To serve

About 85g (3oz) blueberries

Icing sugar

1 Put the digestives in a freezer bag and crush to fine crumbs with a rolling pin. Stir the crumbs into the melted butter. Divide among four individual 7.5cm (3in) diameter loose-bottomed flan tins and press the crumbs evenly over the bottom.

2 Put the cream cheese in a bowl and beat to soften slightly. Add the yogurt, lime zest and juice, and sugar, and beat to combine. Whip the cream in a separate bowl until it makes soft peaks, then fold into the cream cheese mixture.

3 Spoon the filling into the tins over the crumb bases. Cover and chill for at least 2 hours, or overnight, to set. Or freeze the cheesecakes; when needed, thaw overnight in the fridge.

4 Remove the side from each tin, then use a palette knife to carefully lift the cheesecake from the tin bottom and place on a plate. Top each cheesecake with blueberries and dust with sifted icing sugar before serving.

PREPARATION TIME 20 MINUTES | COOKING TIME 16–18 MINUTES | MAKES ABOUT 30

oat and raisin cookies

Oats are a **good source of tryptophan**, which can raise the levels of serotonin and help with sleep. Raisins are a good source of magnesium, which also **aids sleep**.

115g (4oz) butter, at room temperature

100g (3½oz) soft light brown sugar

75g (2½oz) caster sugar

1 egg, beaten

1 tsp vanilla extract

150g (5½oz) rolled oats

150g (5½oz) wholemeal or white plain flour

½ tsp ground cinnamon

½ tsp baking powder

¼ tsp salt

125g (4½oz) raisins

1 Preheat the oven to 180°C (160°C fan), gas 4. Beat the butter and the sugars together until light and fluffy. Beat in the egg and vanilla extract. Mix together the oats, flour, cinnamon, baking powder, and salt, then stir this into the butter mixture, followed by the raisins, to make a soft, slightly sticky dough.

2 Take tablespoonfuls of the cookie dough and roll into balls with dampened hands. Place the balls, spaced well apart, on two baking sheets lined with baking parchment. Flatten the balls slightly with your fingers or with a fork dusted with flour.

3 Bake the cookies for 16–18 minutes until lightly golden. Remove from the oven and leave to cool on the baking sheets for 10 minutes, then transfer to a cooling rack using a palette knife or fish slice. Allow to cool completely. The cookies will firm slightly as they cool but will still remain soft.

4 Store the cookies in an airtight tin or box. Or freeze in sealable plastic bags or boxes; thaw at room temperature for 1–2 hours when needed.

PREPARATION TIME 25–30 MINUTES, PLUS 1–2 HOURS CHILLING | COOKING TIME 9 MINUTES | MAKES ABOUT 30

ginger biscuit shapes

It is fun to use **various novelty cutters**, such as stars, circles, and flowers, so that your baby can learn the names of the shapes.

45g (1½oz) butter, softened

70g (2½oz) soft light brown sugar

4 tbsp golden syrup

1 large egg yolk

170g (6oz) plain flour

2 tsp ground ginger

½ tsp bicarbonate of soda

¼ tsp salt

1 Beat the butter and sugar together until pale and fluffy, then beat in the golden syrup and egg yolk until just combined. Sift over the flour, ginger, bicarbonate of soda, and salt, and stir in with a wooden spoon to form a dough. Put the dough on a piece of cling film and pat into a disc about 1cm (½in) thick. Wrap up and refrigerate for 1–2 hours until firm.

2 Preheat the oven to 180°C (160°C fan), gas 4. Roll out the dough between two pieces of baking parchment until about 3mm (⅛in) thick. Cut out shapes that are about 4cm (1⅝in) in diameter, and use a palette knife to transfer them to baking trays lined with parchment. If the dough becomes too soft, then lift it, still on the parchment, on to a baking tray and pop in the freezer for 5–10 minutes to firm up.

3 Bake the biscuits for about 9 minutes until puffed and just turning golden around the edges. For crisper biscuits, bake for a further 2 minutes. Allow the biscuits to cool on the baking tray for 5 minutes, then transfer to a wire rack to cool completely. Store in an airtight tin.

PREPARATION TIME 15–20 MINUTES | COOKING TIME 12–14 MINUTES | MAKES ABOUT 24 MINI OR 6 LARGE

bomb muffins (banana, oat, maple, and blueberry)

If your baby dislikes too much texture, **put the ingredients** for the **muffin mixture** in a food processor and whiz them together, then add the blueberries and **pulse three or four times** to chop.

30g (1oz) rolled oats

85g (3oz) plain wholemeal flour

½ tsp bicarbonate of soda

½ tsp baking powder

½ tsp ground cinnamon

½ tsp ground ginger

¼ tsp salt

1 very ripe banana, mashed

1 egg

30g (1oz) butter, melted

4 tbsp maple syrup

3 tbsp soft light brown sugar

¾ tsp pure vanilla extract

55g (2oz) blueberries

1 tbsp demerara
   or maple sugar

1 Preheat the oven to 180°C (160°C fan), gas 4. Line two mini muffin tins (each with 12 cups) with paper cases.

2 In a large bowl mix together the oats, flour, bicarbonate of soda, baking powder, cinnamon, ginger, and salt. In a separate bowl mix together the banana, egg, butter, syrup, brown sugar, and vanilla extract. Mix the wet ingredients into the dry until just combined, then fold in the blueberries.

3 Spoon into the muffin cases, filling them three-quarters full. Sprinkle a little demerara sugar on each muffin. Bake for 12–14 minutes until risen and firm to the touch. Cool on a wire rack.

★ **Note:** If frozen, remove the muffins as needed and thaw for 30 minutes at room temperature.

PREPARATION TIME 10 MINUTES | MAKES 4 PORTIONS

first fruit fool

Even fussy babies usually like a **combination of sweet fruit** mixed with **creamy yogurt**. Adults love this too, so you may need to make double!

110g (4oz) strawberries, quartered

110g (4oz) raspberries

1 tbsp caster sugar

200ml (7fl oz) double or whipping cream

½ tsp pure vanilla extract

1 tsp icing sugar

4 tbsp Greek yogurt

2 ginger nut biscuits (optional)

1 Purée the berries with the caster sugar in a blender or food processor. Taste for sweetness and add a little more caster sugar if necessary. Sieve the purée to remove the seeds and set aside. Whip the cream with the vanilla extract and icing sugar until it holds soft peaks. Gently fold in the yogurt, then stir through the purée – it is nice to leave the purée slightly marbled in the cream mixture.

2 Spoon into small glasses, cover, and refrigerate until needed. (The fools can be kept in the fridge for up to 2 days.) If you like ginger, then these are nice with ginger nut biscuits crumbled over just before serving, though smaller babies may prefer it without the biscuits.

PREPARATION TIME 15–20 MINUTES | COOKING TIME 20–25 MINUTES | MAKES 4 PORTIONS

orchard crumble

These easy individual crumbles are **very popular**. To vary them, use **smaller apples and pears** and throw in a few blackberries for the last 2 minutes when cooking the fruit.

2 large eating apples (e.g. Pink Lady or Golden Delicious), peeled, cored, and diced

2 large pears (e.g. Conference), peeled, cored, and diced

85g (3oz) plain flour

45g (1½oz) butter, cut into cubes

45g (1½oz) demerara sugar

¾ tsp ground cinnamon

¼ tsp salt

4 tsp granulated sugar, or to taste

1 Preheat the oven to 200°C (180°C fan), gas 6.

2 Put the fruit in a small saucepan and cook gently for 10–15 minutes until soft but not mushy. Meanwhile, put the flour in a bowl and rub in the butter until it looks like crumbs. Stir in the demerara sugar, cinnamon, and salt.

3 Remove the fruit from the heat and stir in the granulated sugar, adding more if the fruit isn't sweet enough. Divide the fruit among four ramekins (about 9cm/3¾in diameter) and sprinkle over the crumble topping. Bake for 20–25 minutes. Cool to warm before serving, with custard or ice cream.

★ **Note:** To freeze, cool the baked crumbles and wrap well; thaw overnight in the fridge, then reheat in the microwave for 1–2 minutes.

PREPARATION TIME 30 MINUTES, PLUS 3–4 HOURS FREEZING | MAKES 750ML (1¼PINTS)

my favourite frozen yogurt

I adore frozen yogurt and **this tastes so good** that you don't really need any extra flavourings. However, if you like, you could add a **fruit purée such as the summer berry flavour** below. For best results, make this in an ice-cream machine, although you can also make it without. **Simply put the mixture** in a suitable container in the freezer, and then whiz in an electric mixer or food processor two or three times during the freezing process to **break up the ice crystals.**

500g (1lb 2oz) full-fat natural yogurt

250ml (9fl oz) double cream

100g (3½oz) caster sugar

1 Simply mix all the ingredients together and freeze in an ice-cream machine. Transfer to a suitable container and keep in the freezer. If possible, remove from the freezer about 10 minutes before serving.

★ **Variation: Summer berry frozen yogurt**
Gently simmer 225g (8oz) fresh or frozen berries (e.g. strawberries, raspberries, blueberries, or blackberries) with about 2 tbsp icing sugar (to taste), then purée in a blender. Press through a sieve to remove the seeds. Mix the fruit purée with the yogurt mixture before freezing in an ice-cream machine. Alternatively, omit the cooking and simply purée fresh berries, then sieve and beat in about 2 tbsp icing sugar to sweeten. Makes 800ml (1⅓ pints).

PREPARATION TIME 8 MINUTES, PLUS OVERNIGHT FREEZING | MAKES 600ML (1 PINT)

iced banana smoothie sticks

This is a good way to use up the overripe bananas that always seem to be hiding in the bottom of the fruit bowl. For a special treat you can add a little *dulce de leche* (a South American milk-based syrup) to the mix, or dip the smoothie sticks in melted chocolate.

2 large, ripe bananas, peeled
  (250–280g/9–10oz peeled weight)

170g (6oz) vanilla yogurt

200ml (7fl oz) milk

1 Whiz the banana and yogurt together in a blender until smooth, then add the milk and whiz to combine. Pour into lolly moulds and freeze.

strawberry milkshake ice lollies

I like to make this using small probiotic strawberry yogurt drinks.

250g (9oz) strawberries, quartered

350g (12oz) strawberry yogurt

100ml (3½fl oz) milk

3 tbsp icing sugar, sifted

1 Put the strawberries in a blender and whiz to a purée. Add the remaining ingredients and blend until frothy. Sieve to remove the strawberry seeds, then pour into lolly moulds and freeze.

chapter 5

18–36 months:
eating with the family

18–36 months:
what you can expect

Your child will now be **a confident eater**, and will be able to manage almost everything she's offered, although she will probably start to exert her authority and have very specific **likes and dislikes**! She'll enjoy being **a part of family mealtimes**; make the most of her enthusiasm, and encourage her to try **new foods**.

Q My toddler has become increasingly fussy and will eat only certain foods; is there a reason for this?

A Rest assured that this is a normal stage in your toddler's development. Almost all toddlers go through a stage of becoming a little obsessive about their lives, demanding to wear certain clothing, drinking only from a specific cup, or eating just a few chosen foods.

In some ways, toddlerhood is a mini-adolescence, when children assert themselves and their independence in no small measure. Unfortunately, this often extends to their choice of food, which is clearly an emotive issue with parents and carers, and bound to get a good response.

The simplest and best way to deal with this is to ignore food fads and "statements". Continue to offer the same food you always have, and new foods too, and remove what he doesn't eat without comment. When he realizes that his efforts to rebel aren't getting any response, he's likely to give in and resume his normal eating patterns.

Q How big is a toddler-sized serving?

A Hold out her hand and place a few grapes in it. Can she fit three or four? That's roughly a portion, and you can use this calculation for all fruits and vegetables. A toddler-sized portion of protein (red meat, chicken, etc.) is the size of her palm, and a fish portion is the size of her hand. Obviously, some foods are eaten in bigger quantities (breakfast cereal, pasta, rice, and yogurt spring to mind), so don't become too concerned about portion sizes. As long as she is having at least five "handfuls" of fruit and vegetables a day, and several servings of healthy carbohydrates and protein, you're doing well.

Q How can I encourage my child to eat a varied diet?

A The key is to sit down as a family as often as possible and eat a varied diet together. If everyone is eating what's on offer, your child is more likely to do so, too.

Furthermore, it's important to continue to offer new foods over and over again, until they become familiar. Mix new foods with old favourites – try adding broccoli florets to macaroni cheese, or new vegetables such as mange tout and baby corn to stir-fries.

If he rejects foods continually, try different recipes to make the foods more appealing. Adding new foods to old favourites is a good trick, for example, adding mushrooms or sweet pepper to homemade pizza. Hiding food may seem like an odd option, but it can get little ones accustomed to unfamiliar flavours and textures. Children love my Hidden vegetable tomato sauce (see page 179), and have no idea they're eating vegetables!

★ sitting at the table

It's important to include your little one in family meals. She may be able to sit on a family chair with a booster seat, although it will probably take a few weeks to encourage her to stay put! Otherwise, many high chairs have removable trays so they can be pushed up to the table.

milk and other drinks

Your growing toddler **no longer needs to rely** on his "baby" milk for the nutrients that his varied diet now offers, but he may still enjoy **the comfort of regular feeds.** Breastfeeding can continue for as long as you feel comfortable. Full weaning can be a slow process, and it's best to **go at your child's pace.**

Q **How much milk do children need at this age?**

A The maximum amount your toddler needs is about 500ml (18fl oz), but it's important to remember that this figure should also include other dairy produce she eats. So if she gets plenty of cheese and yogurt in her diet, she'll need correspondingly less. Most toddlers who have a varied, healthy diet with lots of dairy produce can get by on about 250ml (9fl oz) per day. Some children meet their requirements from dairy produce alone.

Q **Is there any nutritional value in my breast milk at this point?**

A Breast milk continues to be a valuable and nutritious addition to your child's diet; it's a good balance of nutrients and although your toddler will by now be getting most of what he needs from his diet, it can help to make up any shortfalls. Moreover, breast milk contains your antibodies to disease and will help to protect your child from illness. Mothers produce antibodies to whatever disease is present in their environment, which ensures that breast milk is perfectly and individually "designed" to combat the diseases with which their children are in contact.

★ **did you know ...**

that warm milk will help to soothe your child to sleep? The reason is that it contains a chemical known as tryptophan, which encourages the production of serotonin (the feel-good hormone) that is responsible for enhancing sleep. It doesn't have to be warm; however, many little ones associate warm milk with comfort, companionship, and settling down for the night. Offer it in a cup rather than a bottle, to prevent damage to teeth, and try to rinse her teeth before she drifts off.

meals without tears

As your toddler begins to **exert her authority** in all areas of her life, she will soon cotton on to the idea that food is an emotive issue, and that she'll get a good reaction if she **refuses some foods**, and demands others. Most toddlers experience periods of faddy eating; **remain calm**, and continue to offer the foods you want her to eat.

Q My toddler picks out the vegetables, from his meals. What can I do?

A Lots of little ones seem to have an inbuilt radar when it comes to pinpointing any trace of vegetables, and sometimes fruit, in food. It may be that kids instinctively know that we want them to eat fruit and vegetables, and therefore use them as a tool to exercise their will and right to make their own choices, on the road to independence. My advice is to get crafty!

You can disguise vegetables by blending them into a tomato sauce, and serving with pasta (see page 179), or try adding puréed vegetables to soups, stews, and casseroles. It's a good idea to leave a few "chunks", allowing your toddler the satisfaction of picking them out before unwittingly consuming more. You can sneak veggies into wraps, cannelloni, lasagne, quesadillas, or under grated cheese on pizza. Mix puréed butternut squash into a cheese sauce to make a nutrient-packed macaroni cheese, or mash carrots into mashed potato for a delicious cottage pie topping. Some children also prefer raw vegetables, like cucumber sticks or strips of sweet pepper. Finally, try him with vegetables that he hasn't seen before that perhaps look more fun than a plate of broccoli, such as baby corn or asparagus.

Q My toddler will only eat plain foods with no sauces; can you think of ways to tempt her?

A Sometimes "dips" are more popular than sauces, so offering her pasta sauce in a separate bowl into which she can dip her pasta shapes may appeal, or a peanut sauce for her chicken skewers may work well. Many kids like to see their food separated on the plate, and in its simplest form. This doesn't necessarily mean they don't like sauces, it just means that they like things plain, obvious, and simple, and they like to know exactly what is on their plates. Try putting her sauce on the side, and she may try a little.

There is no reason, however, that your toddler's food has to be bland. You can marinate fish, chicken, and tofu to give it wonderful flavours, and use all sorts of different herbs and spices.

healthy, but not boring

A healthy diet is crucially important to your child's health, development, growth and wellbeing, and it is important to ensure that he is getting **all the nutrients he needs** in the form of healthy, regular meals. But healthy doesn't mean boring! Tempt your child with **fun, delicious meals**.

Q What is the most important part of a child's diet?

A There is no single most important part, as every element combines to produce the right balance of nutrients he needs to grow and develop, and to achieve and maintain good health. Every child needs fats, carbohydrates, protein, fibre, and vitamins and minerals, and all are equally essential.

The key is balance and variety. Balance simply means getting some of each food group in every meal; vitamins and minerals are easily covered by including fresh fruit and vegetables, and good-quality wholegrains such as pulses and wholemeal bread, brown rice, and pasta.

The second element is variety. The greater the variety of foods you choose, the greater the number of nutrients. So try thinking outside the box a little. Offer a sweet potato rather than a traditional white potato, or some corn pasta in place of your normal white varieties. Choose brightly coloured fruits and vegetables, and mix and match them at each different meal. Offer raw vegetables and a dip or a platter of fruit chunks as snacks. Grate courgettes and carrots into sauces, and add pumpkin or sunflower seeds to cookies or granola. If every meal is slightly different, you'll be doing a great job.

Q At what age should I start teaching my child about good nutrition?

A It's never too early to teach children about good nutrition. From the earliest days, you can discuss various ingredients, and talk about why they are good: fish makes your brain grow and makes you very clever; berries make you strong and healthy with not so many colds and coughs; porridge makes you super-energetic and you'll be able to run around all morning; cheese, milk and yogurt make your bones and teeth strong … that sort of thing.

Then use specific examples to help drive the messages home. For example, if she's tired after a hyper high following a birthday party, explain that sugar makes us super energetic for a while, but makes us tired and headachey later on. It doesn't mean lecturing kids, simply using every opportunity to explain why good foods matters.

snacks and treats

Snacks and treats don't have to be unhealthy to be tempting and delicious, and with **the right ingredients**, they can form a nutritious and integral part of your child's well-balanced diet. Used judiciously, too, they **add important variety** to your child's diet, and encourage little ones to experiment with **a wider range of flavours**.

Q **How important are snacks? My child simply can't make it between meals without something to eat.**

A Snacks can be very important for some toddlers who will struggle to make it between main meals without something to eat. The reason is that their tummies are small, and they can't get adequate calories in one sitting to see them through long periods without something to eat. They all need some refuelling, and it is healthy to encourage them to eat when they are hungry, so that they learn to understand and respond to "hunger cues". Many children with weight problems never experience the feeling of being hungry, and are encouraged to eat constantly, and to clean their plates. You'll be doing your toddler a favour to allow her to pick and choose from a snack plate, and to eat according to her own needs.

The secret is to schedule your snacks so that they don't run too close to mealtimes (which can be counterproductive, as your toddler won't be hungry enough to eat properly, and will demand more snacks afterwards), to offer healthy food that doesn't detract from the nutritional value of her overall diet, and to avoid "grazing" (a constant succession of snacks between meals).

Q **Should I allow my child to help himself to snacks when he is hungry?**

A Yes, and no. Most certainly allow him to choose from a selection of snacks at the appropriate time, but make sure you give a choice of things that you actually want him to eat.

Helping himself whenever he is hungry, however, is not a good idea. First of all, it can lead to unhealthy grazing, which means that he won't have an appetite for meals, and it can also lead to overeating – choosing food for comfort, or eating when he's actually thirsty rather than hungry.

It's good practice to allow older kids to choose one or two snacks from a "healthy" snack drawer or shelf in the fridge, during pre-arranged times, as it encourages them to make healthy choices and to eat only when they are hungry. Toddlers, however, do not have the maturity to make sensible choices, and won't understand that a little might be enough to satisfy them.

out and about

As your child becomes more independent, she'll be able to enjoy an increasing number of **outings with family and friends**, and may **begin to eat meals outside** her home. It's natural to be concerned that she's getting everything she needs, but keeping your eye on the overall picture, and using **a little creativity**, will help.

Q What are good restaurant options for little children?

A Given the opportunity, many little ones are very adventurous eaters and will try foods from many different cultures. In fact, eating out can encourage them to try things you may have no luck in serving at home.

Thai food is fun, and many dishes are fragrant rather than spicy, with lots of vegetables, noodles, and rice served alongside. Pizza is perfectly healthy as long as you stick to vegetable toppings, thin crust – and don't overdo the cheese! Even grilled beef or chicken burgers, made from 100 per cent meat, are fine. Traditional favourites such as vegetable-based pasta dishes, fish or shepherd's pies, or even roast dinners are good choices.

In reality, anything goes, as long as you avoid anything that is very fatty, high in salt, and high in sugar, or which contains artificial colours, flavourings or additives such as MSG (often found in Chinese dishes).

Q Are there any healthy alternatives to fast foods?

A First of all, there is no reason why you can't prepare healthy fast food in your own home. Burgers made with lean meat are delicious (see page 181), and you can make your own "chips" by blanching sweet potato and potato wedges for a few minutes, brushing them with olive oil, and roasting until golden brown. See page 184, too, for healthy alternatives to chicken nuggets.

Vegetable pizzas created with light homemade bases, such as split toasted English muffins, topped with fresh vegetables, tomato sauce, and a sprinkling of cheese, are far superior to store-bought and takeaway alternatives. You can easily create chicken skewers by marinating chunks of chicken in any number of ingredients such as lemon juice, honey and soy sauce, or olive oil, lemon, garlic, and fresh thyme. Stir-fries are great fast food, and the vegetables are lightly cooked, so retain most of their nutrients. Baked potatoes with easy-to-prepare toppings, such as baked beans or tuna-mayonnaise make a healthy, family-friendly meal too.

PREPARATION TIME 10 MINUTES | COOKING TIME 26 MINUTES | MAKES 8 CHILD PORTIONS

hidden vegetable tomato sauce

Tomato sauce is so versatile and I always keep a stash of it in my freezer to use **with pasta, chicken, or fish, or on pizzas.** As this is puréed, no one will ever know that vegetables are hidden in it.

1 tbsp olive oil

1 red onion, chopped

1 small carrot, grated

½ small courgette, grated

¼ small red pepper, chopped

¼ eating apple such as Pink Lady, cored and grated

1 garlic clove, crushed

2 x 400g (14oz) cans chopped tomatoes

2 tbsp tomato purée

1 tbsp sun-dried tomato purée

¼ tsp dried oregano

1 tsp caster sugar

Salt and freshly ground black pepper

1 Heat the olive oil in a large saucepan and gently cook the onion, carrot, courgette, red pepper, and apple for about 5 minutes or until softened but not browned, stirring occasionally. Add the garlic and cook for 1 minute.

2 Add the remaining ingredients. Bring to the boil, then reduce the heat, part-cover, and simmer gently for about 20 minutes or until thick and all the vegetables are tender. Stir from time to time.

3 Purée the sauce in a blender or food processor. Season to taste with salt and pepper. Cool and chill, or freeze in individual portions; when needed, thaw at room temperature. Reheat until piping hot, then cool slightly before serving.

PREPARATION TIME 15 MINUTES | COOKING TIME 6–10 MINUTES, PLUS PASTA COOKING | MAKES 4 CHILD PORTIONS

funny-face beef burgers

Your **own yummy burgers** will be better than any fast food, and you and your children can have **lots of fun decorating the burgers with silly faces.** Or serve the burgers more traditionally in buns.

1 tbsp olive oil

1 large shallot, finely chopped

¼ apple, peeled, cored, and grated

½ small garlic clove, crushed

1 tsp balsamic vinegar

¼ tsp fresh thyme or chopped parsley

2 tsp clear honey

150g (5½oz) extra lean minced beef

2 tbsp grated Parmesan cheese

1 tbsp tomato ketchup

1 tsp oyster sauce

20g (¾oz) fresh breadcrumbs

Sunflower oil, for frying

To decorate: peas and a mini
   cherry tomato

Per portion:

30g (1oz) spaghetti or macaroni

3 tbsp tomato sauce (see pages 100 or
   179, or use good-quality bought sauce)

1 Heat the oil in a small frying pan and soften the shallot and apple for 2 minutes. Add the garlic and cook for 1 minute. Add the vinegar and cook, stirring, until evaporated, then stir in the thyme and honey. Transfer to a bowl and cool slightly. Add the remaining ingredients to the bowl and mix together. Shape into four burgers. Cover and chill until needed. Or wrap individually and freeze for up to 1 month; thaw overnight in the fridge.

2 To cook, heat a little oil in a large non-stick frying pan and cook the burgers over a moderate heat for 3–4 minutes per side until cooked through. At the same time, cook the pasta according to packet instructions; drain and toss with the tomato sauce.

3 Arrange some pasta on a plate to resemble hair (spaghetti for straight, macaroni for curls) and set the burgers under the hair. Add peas for eyes and a mini cherry tomato for a nose (or use carrot or tomato ketchup). For the mouth, use a curved piece of pasta (or tomato or red pepper). Serve any leftover pasta in a separate dish.

PREPARATION TIME 25 MINUTES | COOKING TIME 30 MINUTES | MAKES 5–6 CHILD PORTIONS

chicken meatballs with tomato sauce

Pasta and tomato sauce **usually goes down well** with small children. I have added some delicious mini chicken meatballs that can be **mashed into the sauce** if anyone isn't keen on "lumps"!

1 tbsp olive oil

1 red onion, finely chopped

1 small carrot, peeled and grated

1 eating apple, cored and grated

1 garlic clove, crushed

2 tsp balsamic vinegar

2 tsp soft light brown sugar

1 tsp thyme leaves or chopped parsley

400g (14oz) can chopped tomatoes

2 tbsp tomato purée

1 tbsp tomato ketchup

120ml (4fl oz) vegetable stock

20g (¾oz) fresh breadcrumbs

1 tbsp apple juice or apple sauce

225g (8oz) minced chicken

3 tbsp grated Parmesan cheese

1–2 tbsp plain flour, for dusting

2–3 tbsp sunflower oil, for frying

Per portion:

30–45g (1–1½oz) fusilli, cooked

1 Heat the olive oil in a large saucepan and cook the onion, carrot, and apple until soft and golden. Add the garlic and cook for 1 minute, then add the vinegar and 1 tsp of the sugar. Cook, stirring, until the vinegar has evaporated. Add the thyme. Spoon half of the onion mixture into a large bowl and set aside.

2 Add the tomatoes, tomato purée, ketchup, stock, and the remaining sugar to the onion mixture in the pan. Season to taste with salt and pepper. Bring to the boil, then reduce the heat and simmer gently for 20 minutes, stirring occasionally.

3 Meanwhile, make the meatballs by adding the breadcrumbs, apple juice, chicken, and Parmesan to the onion mixture in the bowl. Mix well and season. For a finer texture, chop everything together in a food processor. Dust your hands with flour and roll teaspoonfuls of the chicken mixture into 28 small meatballs that are the size of large cherry tomatoes.

4 Heat the sunflower oil in a large non-stick frying pan and brown the meatballs for about 1 minute on each side. Remove from the pan with a fish slice and drain on kitchen paper.

5 Add the meatballs to the sauce, cover, and simmer
   for a further 10 minutes or until cooked through.
   Divide the meatballs into portions and toss very
   gently with a portion of cooked pasta. Cool slightly
   before serving with extra Parmesan.

6 The meatballs and sauce (without pasta) can be
   kept in the fridge, covered, for up to 2 days, or
   frozen in individual portions; thaw overnight in
   the fridge. Reheat in a small pan or microwave,
   adding 1 tsp water per portion if necessary. Toss
   with freshly cooked pasta and serve as above.

PREPARATION TIME 20 MINUTES PLUS MARINATING | COOKING TIME 6–8 MINUTES | MAKES 8 CHILD PORTIONS

tender chicken fingers

Chicken fingers are **better for small children** to bite into than big nuggets and a marinade helps to **tenderize the chicken**, making it **easy to chew**. I find that puffed rice cereal is a very tasty coating.

2 small skinless, boneless chicken breasts, cut into little finger-size strips

3–4 tbsp sunflower oil, for frying

Marinade

6 tbsp milk

4 tbsp plain low-fat yogurt

1 tsp lemon juice

1 tsp Worcestershire sauce

¼ tsp dried oregano

½ tsp fresh thyme leaves or ¼ tsp dried thyme

¼ tsp paprika

Coating

55g (2oz) puffed rice cereal

30g (1oz) Parmesan cheese, grated

¼ tsp dried oregano

1 egg

1 tsp water

3 tbsp plain flour

1 Mix the marinade ingredients in a large bowl. Add the chicken, cover, and leave to marinate in the fridge for a minimum of 2 hours, or overnight.

2 Put the cereal, Parmesan, and oregano in a food processor and process briefly to crumbs. Spread the crumbs out on a large plate. Beat the egg in a bowl with the water. Spread the flour out on another large plate. Remove the chicken from the marinade, shaking off the excess. Coat in the flour, then dip in the egg and coat in the cereal crumbs. If not cooking immediately, arrange on a baking sheet covered with baking parchment.

3 Heat the oil in a large frying pan over a moderate heat. Fry the chicken fingers for 3–4 minutes on each side until they are golden and cooked through. Drain on kitchen paper. Check the temperature before serving.

4 To freeze (uncooked), cover the baking sheet with cling film and freeze for 2–3 hours until firm. Transfer to a sealable plastic bag or box and store in the freezer. Cook from frozen, adding about 30 seconds per side extra cooking time.

PREPARATION TIME 25 MINUTES | COOKING TIME 20–25 MINUTES | MAKES 8 (OR 16 COCKTAIL SIZE)

chicken sausage rolls

Elevate your family picnic to new heights by serving these delicious chicken rolls instead of the usual sandwiches. Take along a small pot of ketchup for **dipping the sausage rolls**.

1 tbsp olive oil

½ small red onion, finely chopped

1 small carrot, peeled and grated

½ small garlic clove, crushed

¼ tsp fresh thyme leaves

1 slice of bread, crust removed

115g (4oz) minced chicken

1 tbsp tomato ketchup

2 tbsp grated Parmesan cheese

Salt and freshly ground black pepper

225g (8oz) shortcrust pastry

1 egg, beaten

1 Heat the oil in a small frying pan, add the onion and carrot, and cook for about 3 minutes or until softened. Add the garlic and cook for 1 minute, then stir in the thyme and set aside. Put the bread in a food processor and process to crumbs. Add the onion mixture, chicken, tomato ketchup, and Parmesan and season with salt and pepper. Pulse to combine (you can also mix by hand in a bowl).

2 Preheat the oven to 200°C (180°C fan), gas 6. Cut the pastry in half and roll out each half on a lightly floured surface to a 12 x 18cm (5 x 7in) rectangle. Halve the chicken mixture and roll each into a sausage 18cm (7in) long. Put one in the centre of each piece of pastry and brush the edges of the pastry with beaten egg. Wrap the pastry over the sausage to overlap down the back. Press gently to seal, then turn over. Cut each roll into four and place seam-side down on a baking sheet. Brush with egg and cut two small slits in the top of each.

3 Bake for 20–25 minutes until golden brown. Transfer to a wire rack to cool. Keep in the fridge for up to 2 days, or freeze and thaw at room temperature. The rolls can be reheated in a very low oven for 8–10 minutes.

PREPARATION TIME 25–30 MINUTES | COOKING TIME 45 MINUTES | MAKES 8 ENCHILADAS

annabel's chicken enchiladas

Wraps are very popular with children. **An enchilada is a Mexican wrap – a flour tortilla** rolled around a filling, covered with a sauce and grated cheese, and baked. **All my children love it!**

8 small flour tortilla wraps

Tomato sauce

1 tbsp olive oil

1 red onion, finely chopped

1 clove garlic, crushed

½ tsp dried oregano

1 x 400g (14oz) tin chopped tomatoes

1 tbsp tomato purée

1 tbsp sundried tomato purée

1 tsp caster sugar

Chicken filling

1 tbsp olive oil

1 clove garlic, crushed

1 red onion, chopped

1 red pepper,
  deseeded and diced

1 small courgette, diced

350g (12oz) minced chicken

200g (7oz) Cheddar cheese, grated

1 To make the sauce, heat the oil in a large saucepan and sauté the onion for 5 minutes until soft. Add the garlic and cook for 1 minute, then add the remaining sauce ingredients. Bring to the boil and simmer for 20 minutes until thick, stirring occasionally. Season and blend until smooth.

2 Make the filling while the sauce is simmering. Heat the olive oil in a large frying pan and stir in the garlic, onion, red pepper, and courgette. Cook for 5 minutes, then add the chicken and season well. Continue to cook, stirring occasionally, for 7–8 minutes until the chicken is cooked through. Stir in half of the cheese until melted.

3 Preheat the oven to 200°C (180°C fan), gas 6. Lightly oil a large ovenproof dish.

4 Warm the tortillas slightly (in the oven or microwave), then divide the filling among them, spooning it down the centre. Roll up the tortillas and arrange, seam side down and in one layer, in the dish. Spoon over the sauce and sprinkle on the remaining cheese. Bake for 15–20 minutes until bubbling and the cheese is golden brown. Cool to warm before serving.

PREPARATION TIME 25–30 MINUTES | COOKING TIME 30–35 MINUTES | MAKES 4 INDIVIDUAL PIES

mini chicken pies

Sweating the vegetables slowly with thyme and then reducing the white wine vinegar gives **a lovely flavour to the filling.** If you cut the chicken across the grain into thin slices, it breaks up the fibres and **helps make the chicken very tender.** These pies freeze well.

45g (1½oz) butter

1 small shallot, diced

1 medium carrot, peeled and diced

½ small leek, thinly sliced

¼ tsp chopped fresh thyme leaves

4 tsp white wine vinegar

20g (¾oz) cornflour

400ml (14fl oz) hot chicken stock

2 tbsp crème fraîche

Salt and pepper

500g (1lb 2oz) potatoes, peeled and cubed

3 tbsp milk

225g (8oz) skinless, boneless chicken breast, cut into thin, bite-size slices

1 egg white, lightly beaten (optional)

1 Melt 30g (1oz) butter and sweat the vegetables with the thyme for 10 minutes until soft. Add the vinegar and boil until it has evaporated. Stir in the cornflour, then add the stock a little at a time, stirring, to make a smooth sauce. Add the crème fraîche and season to taste with salt and pepper. Allow the sauce to cool.

2 Cook the potatoes in plenty of boiling salted water for about 15 minutes until just tender. Drain the potatoes, then mash well. Beat in the remaining butter and the milk, and season to taste.

3 Divide the chicken among four ramekins or small ovenproof dishes (I use 9.5cm/scant 4in diameter ramekins) and spoon the sauce on top. Cover with the mash and fork the surface to mark lines.

4 Preheat the oven to 200°C (180°C fan), gas 6. Put the dish(es) on a baking tray and bake for 30 minutes. If the pies are fridge-cold, bake for an extra 5 minutes. The tops can be browned further under a hot grill – if you brush them with a little egg white, they will brown nicely.

PREPARATION TIME 40 MINUTES | COOKING TIME 6 MINUTES | MAKES 6 PORTIONS

teriyaki salmon

Eating food on a stick is always more fun than using a fork or spoon (although for small children it is **safer to remove the salmon** from **the skewers to serve**), and this is a tasty way to get your child to eat more oily fish. The cooked skewers can be kept in the fridge for up to two days, and are nice cold, so **good for lunchboxes**.

1 tbsp sesame seeds

200g (7oz) piece of skinless, boneless salmon fillet

¼ tsp grated fresh root ginger

1 tbsp clear honey

1½ tsp soy sauce

1 Put six wooden skewers to soak in cold water for 30 minutes. Meanwhile, toast the sesame seeds in a small frying pan over a medium heat for 2–3 minutes, stirring two or three times. Spread out on a plate and cool.

2 Preheat the grill to high. Cut the salmon into 1cm (½in) cubes. Thread three or four cubes on to each skewer and lay the skewers in one layer on a foil-lined baking tray.

3 Mix the ginger with the honey and soy sauce. Brush some of this teriyaki sauce on to the salmon and grill for 2 minutes, as close to the heat as possible. Brush again with the teriyaki sauce and grill for another 2 minutes. Turn the skewers over and repeat the brushing and grilling process. Sprinkle the sesame seeds over the salmon before serving.

★ **Variation:** Add 1 tsp sweet chilli sauce to the teriyaki sauce.

PREPARATION TIME 10 MINUTES | COOKING TIME 8 MINUTES | MAKES 2 PORTIONS

my first sweet and sour pork

Small children will find **minced pork** a little easier to eat than **cubes of meat**, and they often don't notice that there are vegetables in this dish! **Serve with rice.**

2 tbsp tomato ketchup

1½ tsp soy sauce

2 tbsp pineapple juice (from the tin)

1 tsp cornflour

1 tbsp sunflower oil

110g (4oz) minced pork (or chicken)

2 spring onions, thinly sliced

¼ red pepper, diced

1 ring tinned pineapple, diced

2 tbsp tinned sweetcorn, drained

1 Mix together the ketchup, soy sauce, pineapple juice, cornflour, and 4 tbsp water in a small bowl. Set this sauce mixture aside.

2 Heat the sunflower oil in a wok and stir-fry the pork mince for 3 minutes, breaking it up well as you cook. Add the spring onions and red pepper, and cook for another 3 minutes until the vegetables are soft and the pork is browned. Add the pineapple, sweetcorn, and sauce mixture and cook for a further 1–2 minutes until the sauce is bubbling and thickened.

PREPARATION TIME 15 MINUTES, PLUS 30 MINUTES MARINATING | COOKING TIME 8 MINUTES | MAKES 4 PORTIONS

egg fried rice with chicken and prawns

Most **children like egg fried rice.** You can make it with other vegetables, such as diced steamed carrot, or **leave out the prawns and add extra chicken.**

150g (5½oz) skinless, boneless chicken, cut into small cubes

175g (6oz) basmati rice

2 tbsp sunflower oil

1 small onion, finely chopped

60g (generous 2oz) frozen peas

1 large spring onion, finely sliced

125g (4½oz) cooked prawns

Marinade

1 tbsp soy sauce

½ tsp caster sugar

1 tsp cornflour

Omelette

1 tsp sunflower oil

1 large egg, beaten with a pinch of salt

1 Mix together the marinade ingredients and marinate the chicken for at least 30 minutes. Meanwhile, cook the rice according to the packet instructions.

2 To make the omelette, heat the oil in a small frying pan. Add the beaten egg and tilt the pan so that the egg covers the bottom thinly. Cook until set. Transfer to a chopping board, roll up, and cut into strips. Set aside.

3 Heat the 2 tbsp oil in a wok and sauté the onion for 2 minutes. Add the chicken with its marinade and sauté for 2 more minutes. Add the frozen peas, spring onion, and prawns, and cook for 1 minute. Fluff up the rice with a fork, add to the wok with the omelette strips, and stir-fry for 1 minute.

★ **Note:** Leftovers can be kept in the fridge for up to 24 hours. Add ½ tsp water and microwave for 1–2 minutes until piping hot. Cool slightly before serving.

PREPARATION TIME 15–20 MINUTES, PLUS 1 HOUR MARINATING | COOKING TIME 8–10 MINUTES | MAKES 4–6 PORTIONS

thai-style chicken with noodles

I find that **most children love noodles** and you will be able to sneak in some veggies with them. Feel free to make up your own version using vegetables of your choice. It's fun to let your child eat this dish using **child-friendly chopsticks**, which are joined at the top.

1 tsp fish sauce

½ tsp soy sauce

½ tsp caster sugar

225g (8oz) skinless, boneless chicken breasts, cut into small strips

100g (3½oz) fine egg noodles

3 tsp sunflower oil

1 small clove garlic, crushed

½ tsp grated fresh root ginger

25g (scant 1oz) shallot, thinly sliced

1½ tsp mild korma curry paste

1 small carrot, peeled and cut into fine matchsticks

Small handful of mange tout, cut into fine matchsticks

¼ red pepper, cut into fine matchsticks

100ml (3½fl oz) chicken stock

200ml (7fl oz) coconut milk

1 tsp lime juice

Salt and pepper (optional)

1 Mix together the fish sauce, soy sauce, and sugar in a medium bowl, stirring until the sugar has dissolved. Add the chicken and toss to coat. Leave to marinate for 1 hour. Meanwhile, cook the noodles according to the packet instructions, rinse with cold water, and drain well. Toss with 1 tsp of oil.

2 Heat the remaining oil in a wok. Add the garlic, ginger, and shallot, and stir-fry for 1 minute. Add the chicken with its marinade and stir-fry for 3–4 minutes. Mix in the curry paste followed by the vegetables, chicken stock, and coconut milk. Bring to the boil, then reduce the heat and simmer for 5 minutes until the vegetables are tender and the chicken is thoroughly cooked.

3 Add the noodles and toss in the sauce for 1–2 minutes, to reheat. Add the lime juice and season, if liked, with a little salt and pepper.

★ **Note:** Leftovers can be kept in the fridge for up to 2 days; reheat in the microwave (adding 1 tsp water per portion) for 1–2 minutes until piping hot. If frozen, thaw in the fridge overnight before reheating.

PREPARATION TIME 15 MINUTES | COOKING TIME 45 MINUTES | MAKES 6 PORTIONS

meatloaf with tangy bbq sauce

I mix the ingredients in a food processor **to give a finer texture;** however, **you could just mix everything** together in a bowl.

Sauce

100ml (3½fl oz) tomato ketchup

2 tbsp maple syrup or clear honey

1 tsp soy sauce

1 tsp Worcestershire sauce

1 tsp balsamic vinegar

2 tbsp orange juice

Meatloaf

40g (scant 1½oz) fresh white
  breadcrumbs

6 tbsp milk

1 small red onion, finely diced

2 tsp olive oil

1 clove garlic, crushed

225g (8oz) minced beef or a mixture
  of beef and pork

¼ tsp dried oregano

Salt and pepper

1 Preheat the oven to 180°C (160°C fan), gas 4. Mix the ketchup, maple syrup (or honey), soy sauce, Worcestershire sauce, and balsamic vinegar together in a medium saucepan. Transfer 3 tbsp of this mixture to a bowl, then add the orange juice to the saucepan. Set aside.

2 Mix the breadcrumbs and milk in a bowl and soak for 10 minutes. Meanwhile, sauté the onion in the oil for 5 minutes until translucent. Add the garlic and cook for a further minute. Transfer to a food processor and add the breadcrumbs, beef, oregano, and 2 tbsp of the sauce in the bowl. Season with salt and pepper, then whiz until well combined.

3 Spoon the mixture on to a baking tray lined with baking parchment and pat into a loaf shape roughly 20cm (8in) long and 8cm (just over 3in) wide. Bake for 20 minutes. Brush with half of the sauce left in the bowl and with any juices. Bake for another 20 minutes, then brush over the remaining sauce from the bowl and bake for a final 5 minutes.

4 Rest for 10 minutes before slicing (cut into bite-size cubes for toddlers). Heat the sauce in the pan until bubbling, to serve with the meatloaf.

PREPARATION TIME 20 MINUTES | COOKING TIME 20–25 MINUTES | MAKES 4–6 INDIVIDUAL PIES

cute cottage pies

If your baby is fussy about vegetables **then sauté the carrot** with the other vegetables and blend into the sauce. For younger babies, **whiz the cooked minced beef** in a food processor to get a finer texture.

3 tbsp olive oil

225g (8oz) lean minced beef

½ medium onion, chopped

½ medium leek, sliced

60g (generous 2oz) chestnut mushrooms, diced

2 sprigs of fresh thyme, leaves only

250ml (9fl oz) beef stock

2 tsp sundried tomato purée

1 tbsp soy sauce

1 tsp Worcestershire sauce

1 medium carrot, peeled and coarsely grated

500g (1lb 2oz) potatoes, peeled and cubed

15g (½oz) butter

3 tbsp milk

Salt and pepper

45g (1½oz) Cheddar cheese, grated

1 Heat 1 tbsp olive oil in a large non-stick frying pan and stir-fry the beef for 5–7 minutes until browned and crumbly. Transfer to a bowl and set aside.

2 Add the remaining olive oil to the pan and sauté the onion, leek, and mushrooms with the thyme for 7–8 minutes until soft. Add the beef stock, then transfer to a blender and blend until smooth. Return to the frying pan along with the beef, and stir in the tomato purée, soy sauce, Worcestershire sauce, and carrot. Bring to the boil, then lower the heat and simmer for 10 minutes. Divide among four to six small ovenproof dishes or ramekins.

3 While the mince is simmering, cook the potatoes in boiling salted water for about 15 minutes until just tender. Drain, then mash well. Beat in the butter and milk and season to taste. Spoon the potato over the mince and fork the surface to make decorative lines. Sprinkle over the cheese.

4 Preheat the oven to 200°C (180°C fan), gas 6. Set the dish(es) on a baking tray and bake for 20 minutes until hot in the centre and golden on top. The tops can be browned further under a hot grill, if you like.

PREPARATION TIME 25 MINUTES | COOKING TIME 1¾ HOURS | MAKES 8–10 PORTIONS

moroccan lamb

Here's **a great recipe** for batch cooking. Serve with couscous or rice.

500g (1lb 2oz) leg of lamb, cubed

2 tbsp plain flour

Salt and pepper

2–3 tbsp sunflower oil

1 large onion, chopped

1 large clove garlic, crushed

1¼ tsp ground cinnamon

1½ tsp mild curry paste

600ml (1 pint) vegetable stock

1 x 400g (14oz) tin chopped tomatoes

5 tbsp tomato purée

1 tbsp mango chutney

½ eating apple, grated

150g (5½oz) ready-to-eat dried apricots, chopped

1 Toss the lamb cubes in seasoned flour. Heat the oil in a medium flameproof casserole and brown the lamb all over. Remove the lamb and set aside.

2 Add the onion to the pot and fry for 7–8 minutes until soft. Add the garlic, cinnamon, and curry paste and cook for 1 minute, then add any leftover flour and cook for 2 minutes. Remove from the heat and stir in the stock, a little at a time. Return the lamb to the casserole and stir in the tomatoes, tomato purée, mango chutney, and apple. Season to taste.

3 Set the pot over a medium heat and bring to a simmer. Cover and cook very gently for 1 hour, stirring occasionally. Add the apricots and continue to cook, uncovered, for a further 30–45 minutes until the lamb is tender.

PREPARATION TIME 5 MINUTES | COOKING TIME ABOUT 4 MINUTES | MAKES 1 PORTION

mini croque monsieur

This is quite a generous portion for a child of 18 months but fine for two to three year olds. **The trick is to roll out** the bread slices thinly so that the sandwich is nice and crisp and not too thick for small mouths. **You can also make variations**, such as using smoked turkey or chicken instead of ham, using all cheese, or spreading a little tomato ketchup or yeast extract **plus extra butter on the bread before adding the ham.** Instead of grilling, you can cook the sandwich in a preheated **non-stick frying pan** over a medium heat.

2 slices bread

1 slice cooked ham

Handful of grated Cheddar cheese (about 30g/1oz)

15g (½oz) butter, at room temperature

1 Preheat the grill to high. Use a rolling pin to roll out the slices of bread so that they are nice and thin. Lay the ham on one slice of bread and scatter over the cheese. Top with the second slice of bread. Spread the butter in a thin layer over the outside on both sides of the sandwich, making sure you go right to the edges.

2 Grill the sandwich about 5cm (2in) from the heat source for about 2 minutes on each side until the bread is golden and the cheese has melted. Allow to cool slightly, then cut into fingers.

★ **Variation:** Try making ham and cheese quesadillas too. Sprinkle grated cheese on to a tortilla, cover with a layer of sliced ham, and sprinkle a little more cheese on top. Cover with another tortilla, and cook for 1½ minutes on each side in a dry frying pan. Cut into slices to serve.

PREPARATION TIME 10 MINUTES | COOKING TIME 30–35 MINUTES | MAKES 1 PORTION

muffin pizza with hidden vegetable tomato sauce

My children **absolutely love** these mini pizzas – **they even eat them** for breakfast sometimes!

1 large shallot, finely chopped

½ small leek, thinly sliced

1 small carrot, peeled and grated

¼ courgette, grated

1 tbsp olive oil

1 small clove garlic, crushed

2 tbsp tomato purée

1 tbsp sundried tomato purée

2 tbsp tomato ketchup

1 x 400g (14oz) tin chopped tomatoes

1½ tsp caster sugar

Salt and pepper

1 English muffin, split in half

30g (1oz) Cheddar or mozzarella cheese, grated

1 Put the vegetables in a large saucepan with the oil and sauté them for 8–10 minutes until soft but not coloured. Add the garlic and cook for 1 minute. Transfer to a blender. Add the purées, ketchup, tomatoes, and sugar, and whiz until smooth. Return to the pan and simmer, stirring occasionally, for about 20 minutes until thick. Season with salt and pepper, then allow to cool slightly.

2 Preheat the grill to high. Toast the base of the muffin halves. Turn them over, then spread 1 tbsp of sauce on each cut surface. Scatter over the cheese (or arrange in a pattern). Grill for 2–3 minutes until the cheese is melted and bubbling. Cool slightly, then cut into fingers or squares to serve. For older children you can leave the muffin halves whole or cut them in half.

★ **Note:** There will be lots of leftover sauce, but it freezes very well, for up to 3 months. Freeze in individual portions so that you can thaw it quickly. This also makes a delicious sauce for pasta and it's a good way to get children to eat more vegetables, because what they can't see, they can't pick out. For a pasta sauce, cut down the cooking time so the sauce is not so thick.

PREPARATION TIME 10 MINUTES | COOKING TIME 12 MINUTES | MAKES 2 PORTIONS

pasta salad with pesto dressing

I have made **two different dressings** to go with this salad – the first is creamier; the second uses less perishable add-ins.

55g (2oz) pasta spirals

Dressing 1

1½ tbsp mayonnaise

1½ tbsp pesto

3–4 drops of lemon juice

Dressing 2

1 tbsp olive oil

2 tsp pesto

3–4 drops of lemon juice

Add-ins

55g (2oz) cooked chicken, shredded (see page 108)

55g (2oz) Cheddar cheese, cubed

55g (2oz) cooked ham, cut into thin strips

1 medium tomato, deseeded and cut into strips

1 spring onion, thinly sliced

¼ red or orange pepper, cut into strips

Small handful of cooked broccoli florets

2cm (¾in) piece of cucumber, cut into matchsticks

1 Cook the pasta according to the packet instructions. Meanwhile, mix together the ingredients for dressing 1 or 2. Drain the pasta and rinse well with cold water, then toss in the dressing. Mix in two or three add-ins of your choice. Keep the salad in the fridge until needed.

PREPARATION TIME 15 MINUTES | COOKING TIME 15 MINUTES | MAKES 4 PORTIONS

nasi goreng

1 skinless, boneless chicken breast, diced

125g (4½oz) long-grain rice

1½ tbsp vegetable oil

1 tsp toasted sesame oil

2 shallots or 1 onion, finely chopped

1 small clove garlic, crushed

½ small red pepper, finely chopped

½ tbsp chopped fresh parsley

½ tbsp mild curry powder

¼ tsp turmeric

Small pinch of mild chilli powder

4 tbsp chicken stock

50g (scant 2oz) frozen peas

2 small spring onions, finely sliced

½ tbsp soft dark brown sugar

25g (1oz) roasted peanuts, chopped

Marinade

1½ tbsp soy sauce

1 tsp toasted sesame oil

½ tbsp soft dark brown sugar

Omelette

1 egg

¼ tsp caster sugar

Small pinch of salt

1 tsp sunflower oil

1 Marinate the chicken in the soy sauce, sesame oil, and sugar for 30 minutes, then drain, reserving the marinade. While the chicken is marinating, cook the rice according to the packet instructions.

2 To make the omelette, beat together the egg, sugar, salt, and ½ tsp cold water. Heat the oil in a small non-stick frying pan. Pour in the egg mixture and swirl to cover the bottom of the pan in a thin layer. Cook for about 1 minute until set, then turn over and cook for 30 seconds on the other side. Remove the omelette from the pan and cut into strips. Set aside.

3 Heat the oils in a wok or frying pan and sauté the shallots for 3 minutes. Add the garlic and cook for 30 seconds. Add the red pepper and sauté for 2 minutes, then add the parsley and chicken. Cook for 3 minutes. Stir in the curry powder, turmeric, and chilli powder with the reserved marinade and the stock. Cook for 1 minute. Add the peas and spring onions and cook for 2 minutes. Stir in the rice, sugar, peanuts, and omelette, and heat through.

★ **Note:** Keep leftovers in the fridge for up to 24 hours. Add ½ tsp water and microwave for 1–2 minutes until piping hot. Cool slightly before serving.

PREPARATION TIME 5 MINUTES | COOKING TIME 50–55 MINUTES | MAKES 6–8 CHILD PORTIONS

maple-oat clusters

It's easy to make your own **delicious breakfast cereal** with oats, **pecans, and maple syrup,** and this will keep in an airtight container for several weeks. It's also good sprinkled over fresh fruit or plain yogurt, **or just nibbled as a snack.**

175g (6oz) jumbo rolled oats

30g (1oz) chopped pecan nuts

¼ tsp salt

85g (3oz) soft light brown sugar

4 tbsp maple syrup

85g (3oz) butter, at room temperature

1 Preheat the oven to 180°C (160°C fan), gas 4.

2 Put the oats, nuts, salt, and sugar in a bowl and stir until well combined. Add the syrup and softened butter and mix with a wooden spoon, then draw together with your hands to form a ball.

3 Press the oat mixture out on a non-stick baking sheet, to make a disc about 1cm (½in) thick. Press down well to compact the oats.

4 Bake for about 20 minutes or until lightly golden, then use a metal spoon to gently separate the oat disc into large clumps (the centre will still be very soft). Return to the oven and bake for a further 10–15 minutes. Gently move the clumps around, then bake for a final 10 minutes or until the clumps are golden. Remove from the oven and leave them to cool on the baking sheet (they will crisp up more as they cool).

5 Gently break any larger clumps into bite-sized pieces. Store the clusters in an airtight box.

sandwiches for toddlers

You can **add more texture** for this age group, but not too many bits. Flatten the slices of bread with a rolling pin before buttering them lightly – thinner sandwiches are **easier for toddlers to hold** and eat.

egg and chive sandwich

★ Lower 1 egg into a saucepan of boiling water and simmer for 12 minutes. Immediately rinse with plenty of cold water, then peel off the shell. Mash the egg with 2 tsp mayonnaise, 2–3 snipped fresh chives, and a little seasoning. Use to fill one or more sandwiches.

double cheese sandwich

★ Spread cream cheese over one slice of bread and scatter on 30g (1oz) grated Cheddar cheese. Sandwich with the second slice of bread.

peanut butter-banana sandwich

★ Spread 1 tbsp peanut butter (smooth or crunchy) over one slice of bread, then top with ½ small mashed banana. Add the second slice of bread.

sardine and tomato sandwich

★ Mash 1 or 2 canned sardines over one slice of bread (be sure to remove any bones) and spread with 1–2 tsp tomato ketchup. Top with the second slice of bread.

cottage cheese-pineapple sandwich

★ Scoop this from a tub and use to fill a sandwich.

PREPARATION TIME 30 MINUTES PLUS 1 HOUR RESTING | COOKING TIME 15 MINUTES | MAKES 24

mini jam tarts

It's fun for children to make **mini treats** like jam tarts as they can be involved in the whole process: **making the pastry**, rolling it out, **cutting the circles** and pushing them into tins, and spooning in the filling. For a richer pastry, add an egg yolk and use slightly less water.

250g (9oz) plain flour, plus extra for rolling

125g (4½oz) butter, diced

Pinch of salt

2–3 tbsp iced water

8 tbsp high-fruit strawberry spread with no added sugar

1 Put the flour and salt in a bowl, add the butter, and rub in with your fingertips until the mixture looks like fine breadcrumbs. Add 2 tbsp water and stir with a palette knife, adding more water a little at a time until the mixture will just hold together without crumbling when squeezed lightly. Flatten the dough into a disc. If possible, wrap in cling film and rest in the fridge for 1 hour.

2 Preheat the oven to 200°C (180°C fan), gas 6. Roll out the dough on a lightly floured surface until quite thin and cut out about 24 circles with a 5cm (2in) fluted round cutter. Gather up the trimmings and re-roll as necessary. Carefully press the dough circles into the holes of two tartlet tins.

3 Put 1 tsp of strawberry spread in each pastry case. Bake for about 15 minutes or until the pastry is golden. Leave to cool in the tins for 5 minutes, then transfer to a wire rack to cool completely. Store in an airtight container.

4 To freeze, put the cooled tarts in a single layer in a resealable box and freeze; when needed, thaw at room temperature for 1–2 hours.

PREPARATION TIME 20 MINUTES | COOKING TIME 25–30 MINUTES | MAKES 12

apple-bran muffins

These muffins are **full of good things** like raisins, apple, and bran flakes. They're great for a **breakfast on the go**, but be sure to supervise your little ones when they are eating. For **easier-to-hold mini muffins**, bake in 24 petit four cases for 12–15 minutes.

100g (3½oz) bran flakes

5 tbsp milk

150g (5½oz) apple purée (homemade or from a jar)

1 egg

1 tsp vanilla extract

100g (3½oz) soft light brown sugar

100ml (3½fl oz) sunflower oil

115g (4oz) wholemeal flour

2 tsp baking powder

¼ tsp bicarbonate of soda

1½ tsp ground cinnamon

Pinch of salt (optional)

75g (2½ oz) raisins

1 tbsp demerara sugar

1 Preheat the oven to 180°C (160°C fan), gas 4. Line a small muffin or tartlet tin with 12 paper cases.

2 Crush the bran flakes into a large bowl. Add the milk and apple purée, stir well, and leave to soak for 10 minutes. Meanwhile, whisk together the egg, vanilla extract, brown sugar, and oil.

3 Add the egg mixture to the bran mixture and stir together. Sift over the flour, baking powder, bicarbonate of soda, 1 tsp of the cinnamon, and the salt, if using, adding any residue from the sieve. Fold in, along with the raisins. Divide the mixture among the paper cases (an ice-cream scoop is good for this). The cases will be almost full.

4 Mix together the demerara sugar and remaining ½ tsp ground cinnamon and sprinkle over the muffins. Bake for 25–30 minutes until risen and firm to the touch. Cool in the tin for 5 minutes, then transfer to a wire rack to cool completely.

5 Store in an airtight box for 2 days. Or freeze in a resealable plastic bag or box; thaw at room temperature for 1–2 hours when needed.

PREPARATION TIME ABOUT 10 MINUTES | MAKES 9 LARGE OR 16 SMALL SQUARES

white chocolate crispie squares

These are **so simple and easy**, but I haven't found anyone yet who doesn't love this variation on an old favourite. They are great for parties too. They **don't take long to prepare** and you can have a lot of fun making them with your child.

100g (3½oz) white chocolate

100g (3½oz) unsalted butter

3 tbsp golden syrup

Pinch of salt

100g (3½oz) puffed rice cereal

30g (1oz) rolled oats

50g (1¾oz) exotic dried fruits, chopped
    or dried apricots, chopped

1 Break the chocolate into pieces and put in a large saucepan with the butter, golden syrup, and salt. Melt over a low heat. Remove from the heat and stir in the puffed rice cereal and oats. Fold in the dried fuits. If adding mini marshmallows (see variations below), allow the mixture to cool down before folding these in.

2 Line a 20cm (8in) square shallow baking tin with non-stick baking parchment, cutting the paper large enough to extend above the sides of the tin.

3 Spoon the mixture into the tin and press down lightly with a potato masher or spatula to level the surface. Cover and chill in the fridge to set. Cut into squares before serving. Store in the fridge.

★ **Variations:** Replace the exotic dried fruit or dried apricots with raisins, or omit the fruit and use 30g (1oz) mini marshmallows. For adults I like to add 30g (1oz) chopped pecan nuts.

PREPARATION TIME 1½ HOURS | COOKING TIME 20 MINUTES | CUTS INTO 15–23 PORTIONS

cupcake caterpillar

Here's **a fun and easy idea** for a second or third birthday party. You can expand your caterpillar according to the number of guests at your party, and **decorate it however you like.**

Cupcakes

175g (6oz) softened unsalted butter

175g (6oz) caster sugar

3 eggs

1½ tsp vanilla extract

175g (6oz) self-raising flour

Pinch of salt

Buttercream icing

115g (4oz) softened butter

225g (8oz) icing sugar, sifted

¼ tsp vanilla extract

Red, dark green, light green, and
   yellow food colouring

Decoration

Thin black liquorice lace

1 black liquorice allsort

1 mini marshmallow

2 silver balls

6–8 chocolate mini rolls

Smarties and jelly beans

1 Preheat the oven to 180°C (160°C fan), gas 4. Line 15 small muffin or tartlet tins with paper cases.

2 To make the cupcakes, cream together the butter and sugar until pale and fluffy. Add the rest of the ingredients and beat until just combined. Divide among the paper cases. Bake for about 20 minutes or until risen and golden and the centres spring back when lightly pressed. Cool in the tins briefly, then transfer to a wire rack to cool completely.

3 To make the buttercream, beat the butter until pale, then beat in the icing sugar a little at a time, followed by the vanilla extract. Scoop a rounded tablespoon of the icing into a small bowl and colour it red. Colour half of the remaining icing dark green and the rest light green.

4 To make the head, ice one of the cupcakes with the red buttercream. Cut two antennae from the liquorice lace and a nose from the liquorice allsort. For the eyes, cut a mini marshmallow in half and colour the cut side with a cocktail stick dipped in yellow food colouring. Add a silver ball to the centre and press to stick on. Position the antennae, nose, and eyes on the head and add a mouth in liquorice lace. Leave to set.

5 Ice half of the remaining cupcakes with dark
green buttercream and half with light green
buttercream. Put a line of mini rolls along the
bottom of a large board (such as a chopping
board covered in foil) to make a tree branch.
Position the cupcakes to resemble a caterpillar
waffling along the branch. Make markings on
the caterpillar's back with Smarties, jelly beans,
or thin strips of liquorice, sticking them into the
buttercream at angles. If you like, add red jelly
beans for the caterpillar's feet.

apple and blackberry surprise

This is very tasty, a bit like **a luxury porridge** with caramelized apple and blackberry. You could halve the quantities to make **enough for two children**, but I'd stick to four – then you might get to eat some too!

50g (scant 2oz) butter

75g (2½oz) rolled oats

50g (scant 2oz) caster sugar

2 Granny Smith apples, peeled, cored, and sliced

150ml (5fl oz) whipping cream

115g (4oz) Greek yogurt

2 tbsp clear honey

2 tbsp light muscovado sugar

200g (7oz) blackberries

1 Melt half the butter in a small pan, add the oats, and cook for 1 minute. Stir in half the caster sugar and cook, stirring, for 4–5 minutes until the oats are lightly caramelized. Tip on to a baking tray, spread out, and leave to cool.

2 Melt the remaining butter in a large pan and sauté the apple slices for 3–4 minutes until they begin to soften. Add the remaining caster sugar and cook for a further 8–10 minutes until caramelized. Allow to cool.

3 Lightly whip the cream, then fold in the yogurt, honey, muscovado sugar, and oats. Reserve eight blackberries; stir the rest into the yogurt cream, crushing them slightly. Layer up the blackberry cream with the apples in four glasses and top with the reserved blackberries.

PREPARATION TIME 5 MINUTES | MAKES 2 CHILD PORTIONS, DEPENDING ON AGE AND APPETITE

super c smoothie

Vitamins A and C are good for boosting the immune system, and so
is zinc. This smoothie contains **a combination of fruits** that provide
these vitamins. **I like to use watermelon,** but you could substitute
canteloupe if it is in season and very ripe. **For a thicker smoothie**
freeze the strawberries overnight.

115g (4oz) strawberries (3 large or
   5 medium), hulled and quartered

1 wedge of watermelon or canteloupe,
   seeds and rind removed and
   flesh cubed

½ small banana

3 tbsp strawberry yogurt

2 tbsp orange juice

1 tsp clear honey

1 Put everything in a blender and blend until
smooth. Pour into a glass and serve straightaway.
If there is some smoothie left over, it can be kept in
the fridge to drink later – stir it again briefly.

red fruit rocket lolly

It's so simple to make your own **delicious fruit ice lollies.** The amount of sugar you add will depend on how sweet the fruit is. If your **berries and watermelon** are very sweet, you can reduce the amount of sugar by 1 tbsp.

200g (7oz) strawberries, halved

200g (7oz) raspberries

150g (5½oz) cubed watermelon, deseeded

4 tbsp caster sugar

1   Blend everything together until smooth. Taste for sweetness and add a little extra sugar if needed. Sieve the mixture to remove the seeds, then pour into rocket-shaped ice lolly moulds and freeze.

mango and pineapple tropical lolly

Lollies are always **a good way to get children to eat fruit.** You need a very ripe mango for this easy recipe.

1 x 225g (8oz) tin pineapple (rings or chunks), with juice

1 large ripe mango, peeled and pitted

4 tbsp icing sugar

1 tbsp coconut milk

1 tsp lime juice (or lemon)

1   Blend everything together until smooth. Pour into lolly moulds and freeze.

index

Page numbers in **bold** indicate recipes.

consultants

Dr Adam Fox MA(Hons), MSc, MB, BS, DCH, FRCPCH, Dip Allergy, FHEA
Adam is one of the UK's leading Paediatric Allergists and works as a consultant at Guy's & St Thomas' Hospital in London. He has a particular interest in food allergy and eczema. Adam was named Paediatric Allergist of the year by the charity Allergy UK in 2007.
www.adamfox.co.uk

Dr Su Laurent MRCP FRCPCH
Su is Consultant Paediatrician at Barnet Hospital, London, where she supervizes the medical care of children of all ages, from extremely premature babies to teenagers. A medical advisor to and regular presenter on the Baby Channel, she is also expert paediatrician for *Mother & Baby* magazine. She has also written books on parenting and child health for Dorling Kindersley.

Dr Rosan Meyer MSc Diet, M. Nutrition, PhD
Rosan is a specialist paediatric dietitian from Imperial College, London. She has her own dietetic practice and specializes in allergies, intolerances, and feeding problems. She regularly writes articles for health journals on infant and toddler nutrition and is an expert on several government nutrition panels.

Joanna Moorhead
Joanna is an author and journalist. She writes on health and parenting for *The Guardian* and *The Times* and is a regular contributor to TV and radio programmes on parenting issues, including the Jeremy Vine show on Radio 2 and BBC Breakfast News on BBC1. She has a special interest in breastfeeding and breastfed each of her own four children to the age of two, including her first child who was born two months prematurely.

about the author

Annabel Karmel MBE is the leading authority on nutrition and cooking for children and her bestselling books are sold all over the world.

A mother of three, Annabel is well known for providing advice and guidance to millions of parents on what to feed their children, as well as getting families to eat a healthier diet without spending hours in the kitchen.

Annabel writes regularly for newspapers and magazines and appears frequently on radio and TV as the UK's top expert on children's nutrition. She has several ranges of healthy ready meals in supermarkets, including her *Eat Fussy* range for one to four year olds and her *Make It Easy* range of sauces and pastas. She also has an innovative range of equipment to help parents prepare baby food. Her healthy meals are also served in all of the leading theme parks in the UK, including Alton Towers and Legoland, the largest group of nurseries, and a chain of family-based holiday parks.

For more recipes and information visit www.annabelkarmel.com and www.annabelkarmel.tv – an online TV channel offering parents recipes and a step-by-step guide to cooking healthy meals for babies and children.

acknowledgments

Author's acknowledgments
I'd like to thank Peggy Vance at DK for making it such fun to work on this book; Caroline Stearns for working with me and testing all the yummy recipes; Dave King and Michael Birt for their stunning photography; Seiko Hatfield and Katie Giovanni for their food styling; Elizabeth Jones for keeping my business running while I wrote this book; Evelyn Etkind, my mum, for tasting my recipes – even the baby purees!; Marina Magpoc Abaigar and Letty Catada for helping me in the kitchen; Mary Jones, my loyal publicist; Dr Adam Fox, Consultant Paediatric Allergist; Dr Rosan Meyer, Specialist Dietitian at Imperial College, London; Dr Su Laurent, Consultant Paediatrician at Barnet Hospital, London; Joanna Moorhead for her breastfeeding advice; all the models; and the wonderful team at DK: Helen Murray, Sarah Ponder, Charlotte Seymour, Esther Ripley, Penny Warren, Marianne Markham, Glenda Fisher, and Caroline Gibson.

Publisher's acknowledgments
DK would like to thank Louisa Grey for prop styling; Susan Bosanko for the index; Irene Lyford for proofreading; Andrea Baynham for editorial assistance; Adam Brackenbury for artworking; and our models: Amber Asamoa; Kai Brogan; Lachlan Bush; Dexter Channer; Ava, Humaira and John Felton; Leo Hayward; Tarin Houston; Jas Kang; Hazel and Noah Loo; Elisa and Jolie Margolin; Oliver Moore; Rosina Morris; Nicola Munn; Kyra Nelson; Freddie and Sharon Ortiz; Alex Smith; Aurelia Stearns; Luke and Rhonda Summerbell; Heidi Taylor and Olivia Taylor-Clarkson; Elliot Tripp; Darcy Williams; Daisy and Zoe Wood; Lilyann Yuen-Dent.

Picture credits
The publisher would like to thank the following for their kind permission to reproduce their photographs:
Photolibrary: Fancy 29; Stockbyte 24.
All other images © Dorling Kindersley
For further information see: www.dkimages.com